Investigative Study Into the Relationship Between Gulf War Syndrome and Well-Being of Persian Gulf War Veterans

★ ★ ★ ★ ★

DR. KEVIN C NEWTON

A Dissertation Presented in Partial Fulfillment
of the Requirements for the Degree
Doctor of Management in Organizational Leadership

University of Phoenix

PALMETTO
PUBLISHING
Charleston, SC
www.PalmettoPublishing.com

Investigative Study Into the Relationship Between Gulf War Syndrome and Well-Being of Persian Gulf War Veterans

Hardback ISBN: 979-8-8229-0425-5
Paperback ISBN: 979-8-8229-0426-2
eBook ISBN: 979-8-8229-0427-9

ABSTRACT

Through this study, the researcher investigated the extent of the health symptoms and medical problems associated with veterans who participated in the Gulf War. Importantly, the inquiry specifically focused on the role of physical functioning and diminished health status and well-being. If serving in the Gulf War correlated in unexpected illness, it was hypothesized that the association of symptoms and physical functioning would differ by deployment status to the Gulf War. This study involved a quantitative approach for data collected from 118 Gulf War veterans, with a response rate of 30% from the 362 participants. Through the use of an online survey questionnaire, the researcher was able to assemble a large quantity of data regarding participant characteristics within a short time frame. A probability-sampling was drawn from military personnel who served in the Gulf War between August 1990 and January 1992. Respondents were asked a range of questions about symptoms and health status indicators. Results of this analysis indicated that agent exposure had a statistically significant negative relationship to physical functioning when controlling for demographics, Gulf War Syndrome diagnosis, and disability. Several Gulf War veterans perceived their health as having deteriorated following service in the Gulf War. Results of this researcher into Gulf War Syndrome and veteran well-being may aid in determining the best practices and strategies for the politicians and military leaders making decisions to help Gulf War veterans receive medical care.

DEDICATION

To my mother and father, who taught me determination and strive to believe in myself and to be the best I can be. To my wife Tanya, who has been on this journey from the beginning to the end. To my children – always strive to do your best regardless of the outcome if you know you have given your all. To my work colleagues, who always given me a word of courage during my doctoral journey, thank you.

ACKNOWLEDGEMENTS

My greatest sincere appreciation to my dissertation chair, Dr. Carr. Thank you for your leadership, knowledge, persistence, and reassurance throughout this journey. Dr. Jenkins, thank you for your guidance during my journey and for being straight forward with your feedback. Dr. Rice, from our first conversation, I knew you would be a fantastic addition to the committee. Your military insight and knowledge helped me to reach my goal. I would also like to thank the veteran Facebook group that made this research possible for veterans and future veterans. I also want to thank my entire family for their patience and understanding of this doctoral journey. Finally, I want to thank my full committee. As a team, you brought out the best in me when I started to doubt myself. Thank you. I am eternally grateful.

Table of Contents

LIST OF TABLES

LIST OF FIGURES

CHAPTER 1

Introduction

The Department of Defense (DoD) reviews issued since 1999 have continued to report higher levels of disabilities and deteriorating medical conditions among Gulf War service members as compared to service members who did not participate in the Gulf War. Even though there have been widespread investigations of Gulf War veterans (GWVs), more studies are essential for determining the health impact on veterans who served in the Gulf War (Hall,2008). In the 25 years since the Gulf War, medical investigations for GWVs remain insufficient (Olson,2016). The VA Medical Center in Minneapolis found that veterans deployed to the Gulf War who had been exposed to the highest level of contaminants from oil well fires also had increased rates of brain cancer deaths (Olson, 2016). A clinical, comprehensive examination was provided by physicians of the U.S. Department of Veterans Affairs (VA) for 21,579 Persian GWVs with symptoms or health concerns after the war. Physicians used some psychosocial experiences, including a multidisciplinary discussion method, for a subgroup of veterans to discuss GWS (Department of Veteran Affairs, 2007). All distinct medical conditions recognized by doctors in GWVs were most often indicators. More psychological and definitive diagnoses can be made by increasing the strength of assessments and by combining input of medical information of GWVs. Indications for new or exceptional illnesses related to Gulf War exposures did not emerge from the clinical examination (Department of Veteran Affairs, 2007).

A small number of DoD research reports were performed to determine the effect of veterans' health status (Epidemiol, 2011). The VA's 2007 population-based studies of self-reported physical health did not determine whether or not GWVs had encountered new occurrences of health circumstances from serving in the Gulf War. Conditions of apprehension, reviewed in the Gulf War Syndrome (GWS) and the Health of Gulf War Veterans study of 2009, contained the following categories: physical functioning, social functioning, role limitations, and well-being. However, the veterans who deployed to the Gulf War faced other problems as well, including physical function difficulties, psychological problems, and role limitations within their families. These symptoms made it difficult for veterans to share fully in life activities. Social workers played essential roles in facilitating veterans' health care to aid them in reintegrating back into their families and communities and to return to daily living (Axelrod & Milner, 1997). According to Axelrod and Milner (1997), there are few treatments available for improving the health function of GWS.

Therefore, the goal of problem-solving treatment is to provide social workers with resources to teach veterans how to live with these health concerns such as physical functioning, social functioning, and role limitations (Lane, Tieirsky, & Policastro, 2010). Conducting research on these disorders will assist in determining the best leadership practice strategies for politicians and military leaders of the armed forces, allowing them to embrace the numerous challenges that need to be addressed. Without concrete evidence from research and experimental studies, political leaders would have a difficult time passing laws that would allow veterans who served in the Gulf War to collect compensation and medical benefits (Lane, Tieirsky, & Policastro, 2010). Approximately two years after concluding their service, one in four service members developed persistent health effects in a complex illness pattern referred to as GWS (Carpenter, 2014). As a result of GWS, politicians and military leaders have had to make decisions concerning the health care status of service members who participated in the Gulf War regarding receiving Tier 1 medical assistance from the VA hospitals. Approximately two years after concluding their service, one in four service members developed persistent health effects in a complex illness pattern referred to as GWS (Carpenter, 2014).

GWS-related decisions are different in nature from any other decisions that political leaders must make about GWVs' well-being because of the complexity of medically unexplained illnesses (Science Engineering

Medicine, 2016). For this study, the focus was on determining the degree to which service members had correlations between their different illnesses and their well-being following service in the Gulf War. Like veterans of other wars or conflicts, service members who participated in the Gulf War have not been provided with direct answers regarding the types of illnesses they may have suffered as a result of their involvement in the Gulf War (Science Engineering Medicine, 2016). The different types of medically unexplained illnesses that service members claim was evaluated in detail to include chronic fatigue, headache, neurological and psychological problems, skin conditions, and respiratory disorders.

Research studies such as the annual report of 1999 and data from the Research Advisory Committee on GWVs have been ongoing for the past two decades in order to determine the health status of veterans' well-being (Annual Report to Congress, 2001). As service members still suffer from undiagnosed illnesses, research has been inconclusive regarding the well-being of veterans who participated in the Gulf War (Johnson, Rodriguez, & Solorio, 2010). Military leaders, health care providers, and politicians can use the findings from this research to identify and generate new laws for service connection disability applicable for service members suffering from GWS. Many veterans of the Gulf War suffer from vague symptoms that have collectively become known as GWS (Frost,2000). Accounts of GWS include symptoms of psychological stress, biological contact, and infections. Committee findings from the VA and recommendations about the nature of GWVs' illnesses have noted concerns regarding the broad range of symptoms that span a variety of body parts. In previous wars, medical doctors had observed that psychological stress and sicknesses can lead to the development of higher rates of psychiatric illnesses than are observed in the general population (Frost, 2000). A DoD hospitalization study at the Naval Research Center in San Diego carried out a survey of admissions for veterans over the course of the two years following the Gulf War (Frost, 2000). Frost (2000) found that in the two years before the Gulf War, Gulf-deployed personnel were at a lower risk of hospitalization than those who were not deployed. The physicians from the study concluded that GWVs had an elevated or higher hospitalization for some diagnoses, including mental disorders and blood borne organisms (Frost, 2000). The findings from the VA hospital study were demonstrated to be reliable over time (Frost, 2000).

In 2008, Assistant National Legislative Director Adrian M. Atizado and the Commission on Gulf War Veterans conducted a review in an effort to identify illnesses suffered by service members during the Gulf War (Wilborn, 2009). Atizado advocated before Congress to allocate $60 million dollars each year to study GWS and expand new, efficient medical care (Wilborn, 2009). With this quantitative, non-experimental study, this researcher aimed to validate the outcomes of that investigation. A comprehensive discussion of the research procedure can be found in Chapter 3.

Many researchers have examined the health difficulties described by service members who served in the Persian Gulf War, but significant questions remain unanswered (Null & Flade, 2011). The unanswered questions about GWVs' well-being presents a multifaceted task for investigators of DoD, with a lack of medical surveillance of this population resulting in a large gap in the literature regarding GWS. According to the U.S. Department of Veterans Affairs (2010), investigations completed by the Gulf War Taskforce into GWS issues defined the types of medical conditions – psychological issues, rashes or other skin problems, and muscle and joint pain, for example – that are prevalent in this population of veterans who served in the Gulf War. The conspicuous ailments that impacted GWVs are a collection of psychologically mysterious symptoms that include fatigue, memory problems, and difficulties with physical functioning, emotional functioning, and role functioning. The U.S. Department of Veterans Affairs (2010) concluded that lingering, strange symptoms that occur for one year or more are connected to service in the Gulf War. Few consistent predictors of veteran engagement in GWS treatment have been recognized, and an inadequate number of those that have been identified are attributed to GWS (Frost, 2000).

Different manifestations of GWS by service members has been infrequently addressed in investigative studies, with researchers from DoD relying on data from the VA that was collected and available through governmental data (Flade & Null, 2011). Studies by DoD and the VA regarding

GWS have produced a theoretical approach to the problem of unexplained illnesses (Frost, 2000). Grounding future studies in a conceptual model of commitment may facilitate the documentation of vital, changeable analysis and faster medical and psychological treatment (Flade & Null, 2011). Massachusetts state Sen. Edward Clancy noted that the VA offers extensive medical examinations for veterans who have served in the Persian Gulf War (Kime, 2015). However, Clancy believed a balance should be found between finding causes and providing treatment. In 2015, the VA spent $14 million dollars on treatment. Institute of Medicine researchers believed that GWVs are at increased risk for developing some physical functioning and psychological health conditions such as post-traumatic stress disorder (PTSD), cancer, and respiratory illnesses at a higher rate than other veterans (Kime, 2015).

Background of the Problem

According to Hall (2008), approximately 700,300 service members were sent to the Persian Gulf between August 1990 and June 1991. The U.S. troop deployment was due to the invasion of Iraqi soldiers into Kuwait after Iraqi President Saddam Hussein accused Kuwait of stealing oil near the Kuwaiti-Iraqi border and threatened retribution (Hall, 2008). On July 12, 1990, Hussein began sending Iraqi soldiers to the Iraqi-Kuwaiti border in a massive military buildup. Although Kuwaiti leaders denied the allegations of stealing oil, Hussein decided to invade Kuwait on August 2, 1990 (Hall, 2008). Rempfer (2009) explained that the Iraqi invasion took place over the course of one full day before Iraqi soldiers were in complete control of Kuwait and Hussein declared that he was taking back what belonged to him (Rempfer, 2009). The United Nations Security Council opposed Saddam Hussein's invasion of Kuwait and imposed a trade embargo on Iraq (Rempfer, 2009).

According to Rempfer (2009), the nation of Saudi Arabia was concerned that Iraq would invade Saudi Arabia, based on the verbal threats made by Hussein after the conquest of Kuwait. Some world leaders in the Middle East expressed concerns that if Hussein gained control of the oil fields of Saudi Arabia, he would have control of the majority of the world's oil reserves (Rempfer, 2009). On August 2, 1990, the United States employed the Carter Doctrine, which stated that the use of military force is necessary to defend U.S. interests – in this case, U.S. interests in Saudi Arabia (Klare, 2006). The Carter Doctrine was put in place in February 1945 when the United Nations first set up a province of Saudi Arabia (Klare,2006). In 1990, the United States was committed to protecting Persian Gulf oil by the use of military force, supported by the treaty signed by both the United States and Saudi Arabia in 1945. The United States joined a coalition of 34 nations under United Nations Resolution 678, which authorized the coalition countries to use force to oust Iraq from Kuwait (Lobel & Ratner, 2003).

Operation Desert Shield was launched by the United States and the North Atlantic Treaty Organization (NATO) on August 7, 1990, sending service members to Saudi Arabia as the start of a military buildup of 543,000 troops in the Persian Gulf (Lobel & Ratner, 2003; Rempfer, 2009). Rempfer (2009) reported that Iraqi forces prepared for the U.S.-led coalition attack on Iraq by blowing up Kuwaiti oil wells, causing the atmosphere to be filled with smog from the burning oil fields. On January 25, 1991, Iraqi soldiers unloaded masses of petroleum oil into the Arabian Sea (Sartin, 2000). As a result of these actions, U.S. service members were sent to the Gulf War were susceptible to various chemicals from battlefield smoke and from the fumes from burning oil wells (Nicolson, Bruton, & Nicolson, 1996).

According to Sartin (2000), several researchers who studied GWS reported that GWVs were not in danger of immediate death or hospitalization, but complained of more symptoms and illnesses than non-Gulf War veterans and were prone to seek disability benefits and medical treatment. Initial reports from the DoD investigation showed no widespread sickness and pinpointed no precise origin of GWS (Sartin,2000). Veterans groups disapproved of the inquiry as being deficient, pointing to a lack of information by researchers of DoD (Sartin, 2000). Critics pointed to a conspiracy theory and a massive cover-up by government agencies (Sartin, 2000). During 1996, some news reports recognized that in March of 1991, service members were likely to have had contact with destroyed Iraqi biological missiles in the Iraqi area of Khamisiyah (Sartin, 2000). GWVs then criticized the Pentagon for withholding information regarding known chemical areas and failing to release that information to the public (Sartin, 2000).

Statement of the Problem

There is little empirical evidence currently available regarding the relationship between GWI and veterans' well-being. No existing studies have assessed the impact of physical functioning and well-being of veterans who served in the Persian Gulf (Department of Veterans Affairs, 2010). Despite continuous efforts to better understand GWS, little is known regarding the impact of physical functioning, social functioning, emotional well-being, and role functioning of GWVs (Department of Veterans Affairs, 2010). Many of the service members who came home from the Persian Gulf War in 1991 reported experiencing health symptoms and medical problems shortly afterward. These health problems were referred to as GWS (Ford-Martin, 2005). According to Riddle, Brown, Smith, Richie, Brix, and Romano (2003), the emotional effect of a biological attack, authentic or alleged, can cause immediate and continuing health concerns.

Despite the lack of empirical evidence as to the particular GWS offenders, Gulf War deployment had associations with the existence of hypothalamic pituitary activity and unexplained medical symptoms among GWVs (Golier, Schmeidler, & Yehuda, 2009). Therefore, the specific problem is the existence of a set of medical and health related symptoms on a large subset of Gulf War veterans to include chemical agent exposure that likely decreased physical functioning and that could be related to poor social functioning and emotional well-being as well as role limitations.

Much of the GWI research has been conducted with the goal of identifying the causes, but little of it has focused on trying to determine the multi-dimensional impact of GWS. An advisory committee on GWS concluded there was excess illness among GWVs, but more epidemiological research needed to be completed to make a full determination of Gulf

War illness, or GWI (Lashof &Cassells, 1998). Without this study, GWVs would not have the benefit of research that could help them to support their case for issues they have suffered as a result of their service.

Purpose Statement

This quantitative, correlational, non-experimental study addressed the health symptoms and medical problems associated with veterans who participated in the Gulf War. The researcher aimed to investigate whether chemical agent exposure and other conflict-related disability factors were related to health issues, social and physiological welfare, and role limitations of GWVs. This study was grounded in the past and present literature examining theories associated with depleted uranium poisoning theory, mass vaccination theory, post-traumatic stress disorder, and biological or chemical theories. To meet the target of 118 participants, the survey was distributed to approximately 550 respondents. Survey questions for this study were developed using the RAND Health Care 36-item veteran health survey (see Appendix D). The survey consists of a set of general, comprehensible, and easily managed quality-of-life measures.

Significance of the Study

According to the DoD (2008), at least one in four of the 697,000 service members who deployed to the Gulf region suffer from an undiagnosed illness. The disease is attributed to toxins, to medication distributed by the military, and to pesticides (Wilborn, 2009). Service members may suffer effects from a cocktail of mixtures of depleted uranium, pesticides, low-level sarin, pyridostigmine bromide (PB), and multiple vaccines (Wilborn, 2009).

Through this investigative study, the researcher aimed to answer questions concerning service members well-being who deployed to the Gulf War. Although these service members left the United States in good health, some returned from the Gulf War with undiagnosed illnesses (Foldvary, 2008). Using the results of the study, military leaders may be able to modify leadership development and staff education programs to help government officials understand and address stereotyping from critics who contend that GWS is not an unknown illness. The Veterans Health Administration (VHA) is the largest health care provider in the U.S., but healthcare for veterans may be delayed or be of lower quality as large numbers of returning service members sent health care costs to veterans higher (Foldvary, 2008). According to Bilmes (2007), the VHA will not be able to provide a high quality of care in a timely matter to numerous veterans. Therefore, without increased funding for mental health and outreach programs that make veterans aware of programs, many veterans will not receive necessary medical care (Bilmes, 2007). The government also bears the costs of disability payments to veterans through the Veterans Benefits Administration, an agency that needs structural reform in order to handle the vast number of claims that need to be filed or are backlogged for processing.

The budgetary costs of providing disability compensation benefits and medical care to the veterans of various wars over the course of their lives range from $350 billion to $700 billion (U.S. Department of Veterans Affairs, 2010). There are 24 million living veterans, 12% of whom receive some compensation (U.S. Department of Veterans Affairs, 2010). The U.S. government paid out approximately $23.4 billion in entitlement pay in 2005 (U.S. Department of Veterans Affairs, 2010). All veterans are potentially eligible for service-connected disability if they are found to have a GWS while still in active military service. The compensation payment is made in recompense for reduced quality of life and loss of earnings (U.S. Department of Veterans Affairs, 2010). Outcomes from this research will provide knowledge to researchers and to veterans who participated in the Gulf War. The research may aid in generating the needed funding to provide disability compensation for GWS veterans and providing medical personnel with knowledge of medical treatment for GWV. The findings from this research study can also be used to develop new initiatives for service-connected disability claims by VA management leaders, as well as by military commanders seeking to fairly assess the long-term impacts of GWS.

Significance of the Study to Leadership

GWS has generated debate among medical experts and military leaders, as GWVs continue to present varied medical conditions suspected to be related to GWS. In a research study of 600 veterans conducted by the office of former Michigan state Sen. Donald Riegel, 77% of respondents reported similar symptoms of GWS (Hall, 2008). According to the National Academy of Sciences Institute of Medicine, 65% of babies born to service members after the war had congenital disabilities, compared to the 25% of service members' children who were born with congenital disabilities before the war (Hall, 2008). Babies born to GWVs showed signs of illnesses associated with congenital disabilities (Kennedy, 2007). One medical expert labeled GWS an epidemic, just like AIDS (Kennedy, 2007). As leaders have continued to argue over the likely causes of GWS, some researchers have declared the possible cause of GWS to be sarin gas, advising that more than 30,500 veterans should avoid smoking, drinking alcohol, and using certain sprays (Kennedy, 2007).

According to U.S. Sen. Patty Murray, D-Wash., the VA told GWVs that the syndrome was all in their heads and that they were making it up (Kennedy, 2007). Murray insisted that the VA should conduct studies providing direct links to the potential causes of GWS. While leaders denied the problems, studies suggested the existence of connections between Gulf War activities and the associated syndrome (Kennedy, 2007). Sen. Riegel insisted that leaders must support such studies and inform the 300,000 veterans of GWS findings (Kennedy, 2007).

The controversial nature of GWS in terms of symptoms and possible causes necessitates leadership to support every study finding in the area of GWS (Hilborne, 2009). According to Hall (2008), the government has exposed veterans to experiments involving pyridostigmine and botulism vaccine without their consent. The unethical nature of such research puts the role of leadership into question, with the VA rarely making such findings public.

Nature of the Study

Quantitative studies use variables to measure various aspects of study samples. According to Creswell (2009), a variable is anything that can impact or change the result of a study. Therefore, quantitative studies provide a means of correlating and relating two or more concepts that measure distinctive characteristics. In this case, the researcher applied the mechanism to service members who participated in the Gulf War and to service members' well-being. Kerlinger's (1986) work provided different accounts of variables that researcher can use in quantitative studies, identifying variables using two aspects. Variables occur in quantity and fixed phenomenon or observation.

Kerlinger (1986) noted the difficulty of proving simple cause-and-effect relations in the natural setting of a study. Quantitative research focuses on associations – for example, on the correlations among dependent and independent variables. Independent variables are those variables that are assumed to influence or cause the results (Kerlinger, 1986). Some researchers refer to independent variables as predictors or as manipulated or antecedent variables (Creswell, 2009). Dependent variables, on the other hand, are those variables assumed to represent the results or outcomes of the independent variables (Kerlinger, 1986). Creswell (2009) explained that scholars must identify the relationships between the variables and how the variables will be detected or measured. The use of variables in a quantitative study serves to relate and compare the samples in the survey (Creswell, 2009).

For this study, the researcher used linear regression or correlation to measure the variables of social functioning, emotional functioning, and physical role functioning associated with another measurement variable. Specifically, the linear regression or correlation measured the strength of the associations or the equivalences that defined the associations and served to forecast unknown values. The researcher also chose correlation and regression as a means of evaluating the strength of the connections among the social functioning, emotional functioning, and physical role functioning variables, thereby showing how close the points on the graph were to the regression line.

The background information for the current study was used to investigate veterans' health conditions before and after participating in the Gulf War and to examine information about health complications and experiences during the war. The clarification of background factors was necessary for establishing the factors that contributed to differences between veterans who were physically in the Persian Gulf and veterans who remained stateside. For this study, GWVs were presented with opportunities to identify health issues of concern to them during and after the Gulf War in connection with physical, social, emotional, and role functioning. The findings revealed the impact of exposures on service members who served in the Gulf War and provided insight concerning their long-term well-being.

These findings have the potential to impact veteran health policies and disability compensation. The VA policy for service members states that if a service member is found to have GWS, he or she will be deemed to have a service-connected qualifying chronic disability (Department of Veterans Affairs, 2010). The determination of GWS makes it easier to obtain disability benefits from the VA for injuries during service. In addition to being qualified for compensation from the VA, disabled veterans can also qualify for Social Security disability benefits (Department of Veterans Affairs, 2010). The Veteran Affairs of Public Health and Office of Research and Development agency actively supports investigations that focus on understanding, successfully identifying, and treating health problems, including those resulting from the theoretically harmful elements from which Gulf War service members were unprotected (Valdes, 2000).

Research Questions

Research questions for this study targeted the broad issues that must be addressed in order to understand the everyday phenomena of GWS exposure, disabilities, and physical functioning and in order to determine how those phenomena are related to the social, emotional, and role functioning of post-Gulf War veterans (Creswell, 2007). Creswell (2007) noted that a thought-out and concentrated research question leads directly to the study hypothesis and that a working hypothesis provides insight into the study question.

Demographic factors are personal characteristics used to gather and evaluate data on individuals in each population (Cohen, 1998). Typical demographic factors include age, gender, marital status, race, education, income, and occupation. Cohen (1998) noted that researchers study the demographic makeup of a population in order to determine the growth of communities and shared experiences. This research included demographic categories of age, gender, race/ethnicity, marital status, and socioeconomic status.

Research Question 1

RQ1: To what extent is chemical agent exposure related to physical functioning for veterans who suffered from GWS when controlling for demographic factors?

The null and alternative hypotheses were as follows:

$H1_0$: There is no association between chemical agent exposure and levels of physical functioning for GWS veterans when controlling for demographic factors.

$H1_a$: There is an association between chemical agent exposure and levels of physical functioning for GWS veterans when controlling for demographic factors.

Research Question 2

RQ2: To what extent does the physical functioning of veterans who suffer(ed) from GWS related to their social functioning controlling for demographic issues such as disability?

The following null and alternative hypotheses were formulated:

$H2_0$: There is no association between levels of physical functioning and levels of social functioning for GWS veterans when controlling for demographic factors.

$H2_a$: There is an association between levels of physical functioning and levels of social functioning for GWS veterans when controlling for demographic factors.

Research Question 3

RQ3: To what extent is physical functioning related to emotional well-being for veterans who suffer(ed) from GWS when controlling for demographic factors?

The null and alternative hypotheses for RQ3 were as follows:

$H3_o$: There is no association between physical functioning and levels of emotional well-being for GWS veterans controlling for demographic factors.

$H3_a$: There is an association between physical functioning and levels of emotional well-being and levels of GWS veterans when controlling for demographic factors.

Research Question 4

RQ4: To what extent does the physical functioning of veterans who suffered from GWS relate to their role limitations due to physical health problems when controlling demographic factors?

The following null and alternative hypotheses were related to this question:

$H4_o$: There is no association between levels of physical functioning and levels of role limitations for GWS veterans when controlling for demographic factors.

$H4_a$: There is an association between levels of physical functioning and levels of role limitations for GWS veterans when controlling for demographic factors.

Conceptual Framework

Foundation and Rationale for the Research.

The current study incorporated several conceptual ideas revolving around the impact of physical functioning and well-being of GWS service members. According to Liehr and Smith (1999), a conceptual framework may be defined as a result of bringing together many related concepts in order to explain or predict a certain event or in order to provide a broader understanding of the phenomenon of interest or research problem. The purpose of using a conceptual framework for the proposal was to facilitate discussion of concepts related to undiagnosed illness, PTSD, PB pills, and the variety of chemicals to which veterans were exposed during their service and that may be related to their well-being. Evidence for exposure of deployed service members comes not from individual exposure measures, but from the accrued epidemiologic associations with use of various chemicals in the Gulf War (Carpenter, 2014).

Research has not provided conclusive data regarding the mechanisms by which Gulf War-related illnesses were initiated by chemicals (Carpenter, 2014), due to the inconsistency of chemical tests performed by DoD linking GWS to chemical contact by GWVs. DoD continued for many years to use technology capable of detecting toxins or secondary metabolites (Carpenter, 2014, p. 34). While several theories are discussed in Levine's (2009) research, GWS theory supports a group of related chemicals, anti-nerve pills, and pesticide theories.

Health Belief Model and Well-Being of Military Veterans

Accessing medical care at veterans' facilities is hindered by long waits. Additional barriers frustrate military veterans attempting to get care and influence their well-being. Through this study, therefore, the researcher sought to determine whether there was a causal, link between GWS and long-term impact of GWS on the well-being of GWVs.

The Health Belief Model is a psychological theory used to predict and analyze health behaviors (Pietrzak, Johnson, Goldstein, Malley, &

Southwick, 2009), and as such, is applicable to this study. The model depicts the isolation after the Gulf War as a factor influencing health-seeking behavior among military veterans and contributing to personal beliefs based on the Health Belief Model (Pietrzak et al., 2009). The Health Belief Model could be used to explain the needs of veterans in the society and to identify the factors limiting their well-being, health-seeking actions, and behaviors. The themes in the model portray the barriers, including stigma and social exclusion, limited motivation, social practices, basic human wants, and academic research competing with health requirements. Veterans undergo a broad range of individual, social, and logistical problems in accessing services (Stecker, Fortney, Hamilton, & Ajzen, 2007). Providing high standards of health care services for military veterans is a U.S. government priority (U.S. Department of Defense, 2007). The waiting times for medical treatment have been a focus of attention, but little attention has been paid to other related factors that create difficulty for veterans seeking medical treatment.

Due to personal attitudes of disconnection, civilians considered the stigma that comes with the veteran status as working against them in seeking health treatment. As a result, veterans hesitate to access health services that they see as potentially excluding them from the society (Sledge,2016). Veterans are quoted as admitting that they cannot confess what occurred during the war to anyone because that would cost them their jobs (Sledge,2016). Veterans are even concerned about sharing information regarding health issues on social platforms, being reluctant to make such information public (Vogt, 2011). Veterans express concern that the events they experienced during times of war can be used against them and can lead to a life of stigmatization. Veterans can be motivated to boost their health care involvement as a result of individual beliefs. Veterans reported feelings of exclusion after returning from the Gulf War, with those feelings affecting general well-being and their health-related perceptions (Vogt, 2011). Veterans' personal beliefs impact their emotional and physical conditions and their willingness to seek medical care (Vogt, 2011). Veterans have admitted that their life experiences in the military disconnected them from normal life, placing their social and mental status captive to experiences out on the battlefield (Vogt, 2011). Some veterans confessed neglecting health care issues in the face of finding it challenging to remain physically fit as a result of limited access to facilities (Vogt, 2011).

Veterans have the impression of being left to recover by themselves without any military assistance. Generational differences between the veterans of the various wars also contribute to feelings of disconnection after active duty. In addition, the emphasis on self-reliance within the military culture leads to further isolation regardless of whether emotional and health needs are being fulfilled. Veterans observe that the military value of independence causes them to shy away from seeking help (Vogt, 2011). Some veterans who were known to be very social, have become antisocial. Because GWVs who may suffer with PTSD are not used to open interactions, they find it hard to fit back into normal social settings (Vogt, 2011). Often, veterans have been trained to avoid any form of dependence and therefore tend to detach themselves and seek comfort in solitude (Vogt, 2011). In terms of personal and family needs, priority is often placed on veterans' food, clothing, and shelter, with veterans' health needs taking a back seat. Veterans view employment as a necessity, often deciding that they can compromise the state of their health in order to acquire jobs. As they seek sustainable jobs, they avoid exposing past injuries that might deprive them of work opportunities. Veterans may be motivated to apply for health care in order to take care of family needs, but find the cost of health services to be unaffordable and find access to be limited. For example, veteran healthcare services are generally limited to the business hours during which veterans can be working to provide for their families.

Academic issues also become modifying factors. Veterans may attend school in order to interact with other people and to move out of solitude, but find it laborious and difficult to balance academic pursuits with the priorities of an ordinary life. Many veterans report that the simply cannot fulfill their roles with their families, pursue their work responsibilities, and attend classes at the same time. PTSD and other physical difficulties make such situations challenging as well (Sayer et. al., 2009). The influence of social and individual determinants of health – stress, the feeling of stigma, and the dissatisfaction of human needs, for example –are substantial (Sayer et. al., 2009). Improving access to health and better living standards could ease veterans' adaptation to civilian life.

Conspiracy Theory

GWS is comprised of a variety of diseases amongst service members, ranging from common ailments to very severe sicknesses. GWS has a wide range of symptoms and many unconnected conditions (Epidemiol, 2011). Problems such as irritable bowel syndrome, sleep disturbances, night sweating, and body aches are among the symptoms that are often clustered together (Epidemiol, 2011). According to Venkatraman, Huettel, Chuah, Payne, & Chee (2011), something is happening physically and mentally with GWVs, noting that service members are suffering from many functioning difficulties and emotional illnesses instead of from one particular disease.

Gulf War Mystery

According to O'Regan (2007), there are still no answers to the unknown aspects of GWS. Many psychotherapists believe that the final solution will entail biological ordnances contact in some manner, but most external researchers think military officials are guessing regarding the illnesses of service members who served in the Gulf War (O'Regan,2007). According to Levine (2009), one explanation is that some service members' documentation of duty in the Gulf War is misplaced. Analysts of GWS supposed that Gulf War service members were vaccinated with an antidote that created a surplus pathogens or adverse effect to service members' well-being (Levine,2009). Although this may be correct about the vaccines, more investigation should be completed to decide what effects the antidote had on service members.

Panel Finds Widespread Gulf War Syndrome

Reports have showed that half of the members of the armed forces serving in the 1991 Gulf War endured multiple warning signs of health problems caused by contact with or exposure to toxic chemicals at some stage during the Gulf War. GWS is characteristically distinguished by an amalgamation of concentration and memory difficulty, constant headaches, unexplained fatigue, and general pain compared to those service members who did not serve in the Persian Gulf. GWS also includes ongoing digestive problems, skin lesions, and respiratory problems (Stephey, 2008). Half of the Gulf War service members used PB pills during Operation Desert Storm while serving in the Gulf region; while the highest use was among those in advance combat areas. Service members who did not serve in the Persian Gulf did not take PB (Stephey, 2008). Numerous service members reported that they were required to take pills that had not gained the prior approval of the Food and Drug Administration (Stephey, 2008). Some of the members stated upon taking the pills, they instantly became ill (Stephey, 2008).

Studying the different illnesses associated with GWS may help in determining their causes, as well as the relationships of these illnesses to the war environment as compared to those service members who did not serve in the Gulf War. GWS symptoms and conditions may be determined to be highly associated with one another. Considering that the GWVs acquired the illnesses after deployment in the war zone, it may indicate that common risk factors exist dependent upon the war environment and actions that may contribute to GWS (Rand, 2009).

Chemical Cause

An evaluation of medical studies by DoD on GWS suggested the mysterious disorders were brought about by various related chemicals that were present in pesticides used within military facilities and in anti-nerve gas pills that service members had been given (Chong, 2008). The results from the DoD report were supported by recent research that assessed the significant illness associations with the deployment characteristics of GWVs (Steele, Sastre, Gerkovich, & Cook, 2012). Wartime experiences were compared as narrated by GWVs. The base population sample was 304 veterans comprised of 144 cases that met pre-established GWS criteria, and 160-control group of veterans showed no symptoms GWS.

The results showed that among service members who were deployed in combat areas, GWS had the strongest associations with the use of PB pills and with working inside a two-mile proximity of scud missiles exploding.

GWS was found to be only significantly related to the personal use of pesticides among the veterans who only stayed in maintenance areas (Steele et al., 2012). Prevalence was high among the smaller units that put on uniforms preserved with pesticide, most of whom also used skin pesticides. A significant association between combat service and GWS was not discovered in the study, although the etiology of GWS is considerable, with suggestions of links to some wartime exposures such as Vietnam (Steele et al., 2012).

Another theory from some researcher and service members who served in the Persian Gulf is that GWVs were infected by their advanced weapons. Some military vehicles and missiles were coated with depleted uranium, a result of the substance that ignites chemical weapons. Since depleted uranium is bullet proof, it helps shield aircraft and M1 armored tanks from hostile fire, and missiles that are covered with it can perforate army tanks like a knife. Depleted uranium generally presents little hazard to the public, but is released on contact and can cause harm to people in a catastrophic way (Steele et al., 2012).

Functional and Emotional Impact of Gulf War

The military is the common context for practical and emotional stressors. To fully understand how the theoretical framework contributes to understanding the well-being of Persian Gulf veterans, an understanding of the nature of the military is needed. Some groups, due to social location, may be more vulnerable than others and may demonstrate their functional and emotional reactions differently (Tucker-Drob, 2011). Without various indicators of stress, it is possible to incorrectly overstate the vulnerability of some groups, while at the same time underestimating the general impact of the wellbeing of service members under examination.

There is an indication that service members who returned to private life shortly after the Gulf War had greater adjustment difficulties than those who remained associated with the military. Veterans who remained in the military may have war reactions such as depression, but they may not feel as isolated since they are in an environment that on the surface appears to be supportive and provides an opportunity to interact daily with others who may have also experienced a war conflict. However, veterans who were discharged to civilian life after the Gulf War may have more frequently encountered ill health.

While some Gulf War service members experienced significant PTSD, others may experience a host of emotional and physical functioning problems as a result of their war experiences. Early reports concerning GWVs found that they experienced some physical health illnesses, as well as feelings of depression, guilt, shame, marriage problems, increased anger and isolation, a reluctance to change, and an over-reaction to change (Tucker-Drob, 2011). For this study, the researcher used self-reported physical health concerns of the veterans, as well as self-reported feelings of depression and aggression, to assess emotional health. Both physical and emotional stress outcomes were studied.

Post-Traumatic Stress Disorder

GWS is a disorder with many symptoms. It exhibits unexplainable symptoms by the standard clinical diagnoses, apart from hypothesized external causative agents as to its etiology, psychological stress is also a proposed causal theory (Chong, 2008). A previous study by DoD evaluated brain abnormalities associated with the GWS and suggested that veterans experiencing GWS had concentrated levels of N-acetylaspartate, the neurological marker NAA, in the basal ganglia and pons (Haley et al., 2000). Although another study conducted regarding identifying the relationship among GWS, brain NAA, and PTSD did not observe changes in brain NAA levels and ratios. The findings revealed a higher prevalence of PTSD and its symptoms among the GWVs. The researchers concluded that symptom complexity is due to psychological stress in the veterans' deployment and not due to the damage of neurons in the basal ganglia or to war injuries (Weiner et al., 2011).

Other studies addressed the prevalence and correlates of PTSD among Gulf War-deployed personnel in terms of their levels of involvement in the war (Al-Turkait & Ohaeri, 2008). The degrees of exposure to war trauma were explored as compared to that of service members who were not exposed to war. From a psychological viewpoint of the results from the RAND Cooperation PTSD study, PTSD was found to have been caused by the continued threat from Iraq and exposure to the eponymous operational theater of war (RAND,2016). The veterans believed their life decisions were controlled by environmental factors that they could not influence, such as the war situation, with those beliefs founds to have an impact on their physical and well-being (RAND,2016). Another study by DoD found contradicting results, concluding that combat and interpersonal trauma exposure negatively related to the mental health of post-deployed female veterans (Hassija, Jakupack, Maguen, & Shipherd, 2012).

PTSD theory is important because relationships between psychological and physical health are increasingly recognized (Abouzeid, Kelsall, Forbes, Sim, & Creamer, 2012). PTSD is associated with medical conditions from cardiovascular to respiratory and gastrointestinal disorders and other physically mysterious mental disorders such as unexplained vertigo and migraines (Gupta, 2013). Immune-mediated disorders, or disorders that occur when the body's immune system fails, are also common co-morbidities with PTSD.

PTSD has implications for emotional instability and has been found to alter certain parts of the brain that are related to the nervous and antibodies functions of the central and autonomic systems (Gupta, 2013). As GWVs experienced a high prevalence of psychopathologies like PTSD and other undiagnosed illnesses, it can be posited that PTSD led to other GWS symptoms. This study has assessed the psychological symptomatology of theories associated with mental health and well-being of GWVs. In particular, PTSD symptomology provides insight into the short and long-term symptoms of PTSD in GWVs (Abouzeid et al., 2012). The war veterans with histories of PTSD had increased risks of acquiring hypertension, which was a condition found to be more prevalent in Gulf War-deployed veterans who had returned from war than in those service members who did not serve in combat during the Gulf War.

Definition of Terms

The terms below are defined as they are used for the present study. The terms are used throughout the study in relationship to GWS.

Well-being: The term well-being describes an individual's social, emotional, and role functioning (Merriam Webster, 2014).

Agent exposure: Agent exposure refers to the chemicals to which veterans were exposed and the severity of the exposits, with direct symptoms and possible lasting medical conditions depend on the degree of exposure (Merriam Webster, 2014).

Physical functioning: Physical functioning refers to the simple and complex activities that are considered crucial for continuing stability, as well as to those that are considered optional for living alone (Merriam Webster, 2014).

Social functioning: An individual's social functioning is his or her capacity for intermingling easily and effectively with individuals or groups (Merriam Webster, 2014).

Emotional functioning: Emotional functioning is evidenced by a mental or behavioral disorder, including unsettled emotional injury result of rejection or inappropriate criticism (Merriam Webster, 2014).

Role functioning: Role functioning refers to the privileges, responsibilities, and likely activities patterns that are related to specific societal positions (Merriam Webster, 2014).

Gulf War Syndrome (GWS): Gulf War Syndrome, or GWS, is the label given to a variety of medical illnesses suffered by veterans who served in the conflicts in the Persian Gulf region (Levine, 2009).

Neurocognitive: The term neurocognitive describes cognitive functions (Merriam Webster, 2014).

Post-traumatic stress disorder (PTSD): Post-traumatic stress disorder, or PTSD, refers to psychological stresses such as those encountered in war or resulting from violence (Levine, 2009).

Assumptions

The underlying beliefs or assumptions that form the foundation of a research study are often taken for granted by researchers. To define and strengthen their studies, researcher should recognize the assumptions being made in the research (Walker, 2003). Walker (2003) suggested that all research studies are identified through ideal fit, conceptual consistency, operational logic, empirical evidence, and research value. The fundamental assumptions of this research study are outlined below.

- According to Stewart, Hays and Ware (1992), the Rand Health Care 36-item survey measures functioning and well-being of self-reported health-care. The Rand Health Care (2012) 36-item survey aids researchers and doctors in determining outcomes and in finding out how patients fare with medical treatments. Researchers also use the survey to monitor the chronically ill as well to construct health measures that can be used individually or as a set. The measures documented by the survey are comprehensive, reflecting a full range of health concerns of patients.

- The Rand Health Care (2012) survey is a sufficient tool for accurately measuring the relationship between the degree of service members' assertions of physical, social, emotional and role functioning.

- The data obtained from the participants will be both reliable and valid.

A researcher must ensure that all study participants understand the goals and process involved in the study. The researcher expected participants to understand the processes involved in this study and to possess the abilities and skills necessary for participating in this study. Three key operational assumptions are outlined below.

- The instructions provided to participants will ensure the accuracy of responses from members.

- The participants have the skills and abilities necessary for understanding and following the processes as explained.

- The scope of the research problem is sufficient for determining whether a relationship exists between the illnesses displayed by those veterans who served in the Gulf War and the illnesses displayed by those who did not.

The researcher sought to ensure that the questionnaire used to survey participants was adequate for measuring the research problem. The researcher also attempted to ensure that the scope of the survey would be sufficient for measuring the research question. The researcher formulated researcher questions aimed at testing theories and making application to real situation.

In research, errors can occur at any stage. Problems can manifest during the research design process, in the process of defining variables, during the investigation and information-gathering stages, and during the process of interpreting investigation findings. In this case, the researcher hypothesized that reliable information from war veterans would be obtained. As Neumann and Robson (2012) indicated, researchers must guard against possible errors or obstacles that may interfere with the inferences from the data.

Scope

For this study, the researcher focused on the health status of service members who served in the Gulf War between August 1990 and January 1992. The study involved exploring the well-being of service members after they returned from the war. The purpose of this research study was to develop new initiatives for the VA and to enable military leaders to reasonably assess the impact of GWS on service members who participated in Persian Gulf operations. Many service members have been denied benefits because the VA has not adequately defined GWS.

Veterans who are deemed to have GWS are entitled to benefits from the VA (U.S. Department of Veterans Affairs, 2010). However, veterans continue to have a hard time proving that they are suffering from illnesses attributable to the Gulf War. For this study, the researcher selected a sample of military service members from a population of soldiers who served in the Persian Gulf region during the period of August 1990 through January 1992. The researcher gathered data from a sample of 118 participants for this study, providing a representative sample based on the number of contracted service members who served in the Gulf War. A G*Power analysis was used to compute the effect size of correct numbers of participants as the service members who served in the Gulf War do not characterize the entire military population. Outcomes were not the same for all soldiers in the military since the data described only a selected number of individuals.

Limitations

According to Simon (2011), the boundaries of a research study include factors that extend beyond the scope of the researcher. The researcher identified three limitations for this current study. The first limitation was locating a proper number of applicants for the planned surveys. The second involved obtaining honest responses from candidates during the surveys. The third related to the process of conceptualizing the data. These limitations had the potential to produce results related to GWS and impact their interpretation for the veterans who served in the Gulf War between August 1990 and January 1992. The current research study was a non-experimental, cross-sectional, correlational study. All data were measured at a single point in time. The independent variables did not precede the dependent variables in time order. Accordingly, no assumptions regarding the causal nature of these variables can be concluded with any degree of certainty. The relationships found in this study were treated only as associations and were not considered causal.

Delimitations

Delimitations are used in research to narrow the scope of the study (Levine, 2009). The exclusion criteria of the GWS study was concerned with specific areas that reflect the health status of the post-war veterans, particularly in the collection of data related to symptoms of GWS, ensuring that information was not collected about uncertain conditions of war veterans. In addition, this study was limited by its sample to only those service members who directly participated in the Persian Gulf zones during the Gulf War and, to some extent, to those service members who took part in specific activities, such as destroying war chemicals.

Summary

The goal for this study was to provide newly observed data on servicemen or women, and the health impact of GWS to servicemen and women who served in the military between August 1990 and January 1992. Results will contribute to the well-being of service members who suffer from symptoms of GWS and will have impact their social functioning, emotional well-being, and role limitations. VA leadership should provide support for GWVs by assisting and procuring earned entitlement benefits for service members whose well-being has been proven to be related to GWS.

Chapter 2 includes a detailed review of current literature and historical information related to GWS, the stress of service members, PTSD in combat environments, and the status of service members who did not serve in the Persian Gulf. For the literature review, the researcher objectively and subjectively searched a variety of records for information about GWS. The focus was on locating research dealing with the perceptual manifestations of service members who served in the Gulf War and may be suffering from GWS. Chapter 3 includes a presentation of the methodology employed in this study, including: the research design, the instruments used, the sampling strategy employed, the study research questions, the hypotheses, and the analytic strategy. Results of the analysis appear in Chapter 4. Chapter 5 includes an interpretation of the results in light of the theory, future research, and limitations.

CHAPTER 2

Review of the Literature

In this chapter, the researcher presents a review of existing literature examining GWS, the manifestation of GWS, the physical functioning of GWVs, military vaccinations, veterans' well-being, and the efforts by leadership to eliminate GWS. The literature presented throughout this chapter encompasses the effects of stress on the mental and physical functioning of veterans. Although the literature revealed some of the alleged causes of GWS, researchers expressed optimism regarding the possibility of identifying other factors that have contributed to the suffering of service members from undiagnosed illnesses who served in the Gulf War. The majority of the reviewed literature replicated various types of the illnesses service members are suffering with and the different types of treatments that service members are receiving from the government. The chapter also includes a review of the literature regarding undiagnosed illness and GWS.

Literature Gap

There is a gap in the literature regarding veterans who are receiving health care for undiagnosed illnesses (Martin & Tribble, 2010). Undiagnosed illnesses compromise the trust service members have in the VA. Treatment strategies, and answers aimed at assisting health professionals in addressing the issue of GWS are needed. Studies conducted on GWS treatment strategies included trial studies, however, there is no definitive diagnosis that health officials can determine the cause of GWS (Martin & Tribble, 2010). Veterans can choose where they want to receive care, and some veterans do not seek care from veterans' hospitals because of trust or lack of attention. Another area of research interest is those veterans who do not receive care from veteran hospitals. For this study, the researcher addressed the issue from the perspective of service members who served in the Gulf War and were impacted by GWS. The data gathered from the quantitative, correlational research study may provide leadership with information and may identify ways of eliminating GWS. The data from the VA can be applied to leaders of the military services, by VA hospitals, by veteran service organizations, and by other community support organizations to address the needs of veterans who suffer from GWS.

History of the Gulf War

The Gulf War was an international conflict set into motion by Saddam Hussain's invasion of Kuwait, believed to have been undertaken with the goal of acquiring the largest oil field reserves in the world. Operation Desert Shield was launched by NATO and the United States on August 7, 1990, sending service members to Saudi Arabia and beginning a military buildup of 543,000 troops in the Persian Gulf (Lobel & Ratner, 2003; Rempfer, 2009). According to Rempfer (2009), Iraqi forces, in preparation for the U.S.-led coalition attack on Iraq, began by blowing up Kuwaiti oil wells, causing the atmosphere to be filled with smog from the burning oil fields. On January 25, 1991, Iraqi soldiers unloaded masses of petroleum oil into the Arabian Sea (Sartin, 2000). Because of these actions, U.S. service members in the Gulf War were susceptible to various chemicals such as battlefield smoke and fumes from burning oil wells (Nicolson et al., 1996).

Gulf War Veterans

Military Servicemen's Health

The VA provides services and benefits to veterans who meet certain eligibility criteria. To meet the criteria of eligibility for health care, a service member must be honorably discharged from service and enrolled in the VA's health care system which is responsible for all veteran healthcare nationwide. The VA's priority health care system places veterans in priority groups based on various criteria including disability level and income. Each year, the VA determines whether its appropriations are adequate for serving all enrolled veterans. The Insurance Act of 2007 (H.R. 612) extended medical care to five years from the two years originally introduced by Congress for veterans who served in the Persian Gulf War. The amendment also required the mandatory screening of veterans for traumatic brain injury, PTSD, and any other related health issues that GWVs may have encountered in the Persian Gulf (Ismail et al., 2011).

The enhancement of veteran's programs stipulated in the act would allow veterans who were in a combat zone to receive extended healthcare in order to ensure that they receive healthcare during their transition from military life to civilian life and in order to address medical issues that arise later in life (Ismail et al., 2011). Some GWVs did not show signs or systems of GWS illness until as many as 5-10 years after service. With this initiative, veterans can get the health care they need to make informed health care choices. GWVs may have encounter certain illnesses related to GWS during military operations in southwest Asia from August 2, 1990, to the present day (Ismail et al., 2011). The variety of medically unexplained illnesses that are generally referred to as GWS pose substantial concerns for some veterans who served during the Gulf War.

Gulf War Veterans' Health

Complications from GWS are explained by several authors who researched the occurrence in order to educate the health community and the VA regarding origins and possible treatments for service members who served in the Persian Gulf War (Chartrand & Siegel, 2007; Carpenter, 2014; Caress, 2001). Ismail, Petrik, Wong., and Tabata (2011) and Kang, Mahan, Lee, Magee, and Murphy (2000) reported that service members who served in the Gulf War have more physical or mental issues than their counterparts who did not serve in the Gulf War. GWVs, on average, experience more physician visits and use more sick leave than non-deployed soldiers who served at the same time (Kang et al., 2000). Researchers who conducted studies on behalf of the VA after the conclusion of the Gulf War found that Gulf War service members who actively participated in combat displayed poorer health when compared to those service members who did not deploy to active combat during the Gulf War (Kang et al., 2000). Additionally, Ismail et al. (2011) indicated that GWVs receive service connection disability at a rate of three times that of non-GWVs (Ismail et al., 2011). In addition to having higher rates of physical and mental illnesses, data from the Gulf War registry of 2000 indicated that GWVs experienced unexplained and undiagnosed medical illnesses while serving in the Persian Gulf and after the Gulf War had concluded (Kang et al., 2000).

Australian veterans reported lower rate of exposures than U.S. GWVs, with some researchers contributing the difference to the low rate of GWS reporting by Australian servicemen (Ikin et al., 2004). Since these initial reports, researchers have continued to contribute studies to Australian medical literature reviews focusing on problems in GWVs from several other countries, including the United Kingdom, Canada, and Denmark. However, no available reports have pinpointed a direct link to the Gulf War among Australian veterans (Ikin et al., 2004).

Gulf War Syndrome

GWS is a chronic and multi-symptomatic infection associated with military veterans and workers who participated in the Gulf War during 1990 and 1991 (Blanchard et al., 2006). Since the war, medical researchers have carried out studies to examine GWS. Most researchers sought to explore the manifestation of GWS in order to determine the physical aspect of the infection, examine the correlation between vaccines used on the veterans during the war and disorder, and record the efforts employed by various medical organizations to deal with GWS. The existing literature on GWS revealed some of the causes of the disease. However, researchers in the field continue to conduct research aimed at identifying other factors that cause GWS. Researchers have associated GWS with medical issues such as stress and PTSD.

Cultural and social factors, such as the awareness of GWV's health and causes of disease, are relevant in the emergence of a new syndrome

(Blanchard et al., 2006). As mentioned earlier, GWS is a multi-symptom condition associated with military service during the Gulf War. According to researchers from the NCPTSD (2007), several health issues related GWVs, such as fatigue, headache, memory problems, sleep disturbances, skin rashes, is the most prominent health constraint affecting service members. Several researcher groups from National Center for PTSD, (2007) have been assembled for the purpose of gathering the known facts about GWS to aid medical practitioners in dealing with the condition. For instance, the Congressional Research Advisory Committee on GWVs has gone to great lengths to establish known facts about health consequences of the Gulf War military service (Blanchard et al., 2006). According to the Advisory committee, GWVs exhibit a health condition that differs from veterans of other major wars. GWS is a widespread medical issue that is said to trouble at least a quarter of the 697,000 U.S. soldiers who served in the Gulf War (Blanchard et al., 2006).

The existing research on GWS has gone beyond establishing the existence of the disorder and expanded to examine its expression in the human body. Many researchers have determined several ways that GWS is manifested. It is worth noting in this discussion of the disease manifestation that researcher has, to date, failed to provide any well-established diagnosis of GWS. The diagnosis of the chronic abnormalities associated with the disorder of GWS remains a gap in the field meriting further research. GWS results in a broad range of potential effects on an individual's quality of life. These effects and other impacts on personal, social, and economic life qualify it as a chronic disease (Blanchard et al., 2006).

Based on the existing literature, there are several common GWS symptoms used by researchers to describe the manifestation of the disease. According to Binns et al. (2008), multiple concurrent symptoms such as persistent headaches, memory difficulties, concentration challenges, gastrointestinal problems are common characteristics of GWS. Many researchers also associated GWS with other medical conditions such as stress and PTSD. The previous section covered by existing literature on GWS as the psychological and physical aspects of the disease. As GWS is associated with stress and PTSD, GWVs have rejected the diagnosis of

PTSD, arguing that they do not suffer repetition nightmares. These two psychological aspects are prominent in studies conducted by different researchers of GWS (Binns et al. 2008)

According to Binns et al. (2008), GWVs suffered high levels of distress before and during the war. Research showed that before joining the war, the veterans experienced stress after the release of deployment information. The psychological suffering caused by receiving deployment information was due to the potential separation of the veterans from their families. Besides deployment distress, the National Center for PTSD (2007) identified other sources of stress encountered by GWVs, especially during the war. The center defined war trauma, battle, injuries, and fatigue among the encountered stressors, along with observing the death of colleagues and living under extreme conditions of war (National Center for PTSD, 2007). Most physical aspects of GWS, as covered in research, revolved around blasts, injuries, and deaths during the war.

Although PTSD and stress are associated with GWS, studies have consistently shown that the disorder rarely results from combat and other battle related stressors. GWVs have lower rates of PTSD as compared to veterans of other wars (National Center for PTSD, 2007). Existing research has also established a link between GWS, and the experimental drugs used on service members who served in the Gulf War with the aim of protecting them from chemical agents during the war period. There was a risk of soldiers in the war being exposed to hazardous chemicals used in warfare, but that risk does not warrant the action of humans with vaccines that are still in experimental phases. The vaccines used on the service members during Gulf War may prove to be a primary cause of the undiagnosed GWS disorder. In 1993, Riegle's office compiled a report on Health Consequences of Gulf War based on a wide body of evidence connecting GWS with exposure to chemical/biological agents (McAllister, 1993).

As mentioned earlier, there is no specific, uniform diagnosis of GWS, with researchers from DoD offering a variety of explanations for the syndrome. This critical analysis addressed several aspects associated with GWS, including PTSD, stress, and exposure to chemical agents. While multiple researchers have focused their studies on GWS in general, no particular set of symptoms has been established for diagnosing the illness (McAllister, 1993). Both the symptoms and cause of GWS remain elusive, and researchers from all over the globe are still exploring the disease (McAllister, 1993).

History of Gulf War Syndrome

The difference between the Gulf War research conducted in the United Kingdom and the United States, is that the U.S. government has requested substantial federal funding for research (Lidie, 2018). The U.S. government operates on the presumption that research requires sufficient money to complete research (Lidie, 2018). The Congressionally Directed Medical Research Programs on Gulf War Illness appropriated 20 million dollars while UK officials believe the time has come for the British government to draw the line on GWS research (Lidie, 2018).

A majority of returning military personnel resumed their normal activities with little to no difficulty. However, the number of health problems that occurred was disproportional to the relatively short time of actual combat and relatively low casualty rate (Institute of Medicine, 1996). Twenty years after the Gulf War and many studies later, there are continued efforts to discover the causes of these health problems. Two primary committees, the VHA Office of Research and Development, the VA, and related agencies were assembled and accepted the task of defining the "mystery illness" of the Gulf War (Lidie, 2018). According to Wilson (2008), the cause of GWS is unknown because of the various symptoms service members have reported.

Symptoms

A DoD (2008) report showed that veterans faced many symptoms that were difficult to trace and identify. Not only did American soldiers report a multitude of medical symptoms during combat in the Gulf War and upon completion of the Gulf War, but British and Canadian soldiers of the Gulf War reported similar symptoms (Wilson, 2008). Reported symptoms included headaches, muscle fatigue, nervous system issues, and depression.

Some veterans suffered from chronic fatigue syndrome, characterized by long-term and extreme fatigue that was relieved only by rest (Wilson, 2008). Veterans also faced widespread muscle pain, morning stiffness, memory loss, and headaches. These symptoms resulted in the condition known as fibromyalgia. Some GWVs also suffered from functional gastrointestinal disorders, headache, fatigue, loss of body weight, respiratory disorders, sleep disturbances, psychological problems, and joint pain. Female veterans suffered from menstrual disorders as well (Wilson, 2008). These symptoms of GWS now formed the cases of undiagnosed illnesses when research could not pinpoint one cause for the illness in GWV. The GWVs who suffered from severe health related problems needed attention in order to restore their health. Psychological problems occurred as a result of the stresses of losing friends or relatives. Some symptoms took many years to manifest, making them difficult to identify and treat.

The medical conditions service members experienced after the Gulf War, in terms of both undiagnosed and diagnosed illnesses, have been recounted by service members as unlike any symptoms from previous wars that service members encountered. Whether the Gulf War is characteristic of medically unexplained illnesses, researchers from the National Academy of Sciences concluded that GWVs' health is impacted by an association between illness and exposure (Institute of Medicine, 2008). Whether after the Gulf War medical conditions and health-related symptoms result from GWVs serving in the Gulf War, specified reasons should be further investigated by researchers to better provide an understanding of GWVs and government leadership of veterans' health conditions (Institute of Medicine, 2008).

According to Deahl (2005), approximately 11% of British soldiers reported ill health after returning from the Gulf War. The reported illnesses were similar to the ones reported by U.S. members who served in the Gulf War. Both countries used independent research studies to determine underlying causes for the ill health experienced by service members returning from the Gulf region. GWVs are affected twice the rate with unexplained somatic, emotional, and cognitive warning signs (Deahl,2005).

Environmental Factors and Soldiers' Exposure

Wilson (2008) pointed to chemical weapons as one possible cause of service members' illnesses. Evidence of the exposures experienced by Australian GWVs was not acknowledged in the Australian review (Sims et al., 2003). Coalition veterans from overseas forces were exposed to various pollutants and environmental conditions during the Gulf War, described in several Australian journal reviews (Sims et al., 2003).

Subjection to some of these chemical agents has been linked to adverse health results (Sims et al., 2003). Chemical agents are believed to be a contributing factor to GWVs' health issues because members of the Australian Navy who were stationed on ships were less likely to get exposure than non-sailors who were there during the same period in the Gulf War (Sims et al., 2003). Likewise, many Air Force GWVs who spent minimal time in the Gulf region and had limited exposure in the Gulf War were less likely to have symptoms of GWS (Sims et al., 2003).

Ware and Sherbourne (1992) pointed out that service members from the United States and Great Britain that served in the Gulf War are experiencing health issues that cannot be explained by one single medical diagnosis for GWS. When surveyed, U.S. service members reported a greater number of symptoms and health problems than the British service members who were surveyed (Ware & Sherbourne, 1992). It is recognized that a proportion of the chronic symptoms reported can be attributed to chemical agents and PTSD (Haley, Maddrey, & Gershenfeld, 2002). However, there remain many veterans of the Gulf War with undiagnosed complex symptoms.

Veteran activists have biases, favoring certain possible causes for veteran illnesses while rejecting others. In any scientific or medical research, the introduction of biases will blur objectivity and have a negative effect on research. Many veterans entered into the debate surrounding GWS already predisposed to be suspicious of the government and the DoD in particular as a result of past DoD failings – the Agent Orange issue in Vietnam, for example. By reviewing the existing literature addressing GWS and its combined symptoms, the researcher hoped to support the influencing role for PTSD and other mystery illnesses.

The Well-being of Gulf War Veterans

GWVs have claimed that their health-related problems are related to the service they gave during the Gulf War. To control and treat health issues, an abundance of complaints by GWVs were delivered to DoD officials. Therefore, the DoD created a program called the Gulf War Registry to address such health issues (Institute of Medicine, 2016). The program aimed at treating and diagnosing the GWVs who had developed health problems. Again, studies and research were also conducted to address the GWS symptoms (Institute of Medicine,2016).

Research piloted by the VA after the Gulf War has shown that service members who served during the Gulf War are in poor health when compared to non-deployed veterans who served at the same time (Ismail et al., 2011). The study indicated that GWVs receive service connection disability at rates of three to one compared with veterans of the same time period but who served in the United States rather than the Gulf region (Ismail et al., 2011). GWVs, on average, make more physician visits and take more sick leave than non-deployed soldiers who served at the same time.

Medical State

Some GWVs who suffer from illnesses and disorders can attribute the things they're suffering from to their service in the Gulf War. GWVs were exposed to poisonous gases, for example, such as the sarin gas in the Gulf War, which greatly affects the health of GWVs. GWVs have developed health problems due to exposure to these harmful gases, which led to a development of infectious diseases, skins diseases, and respiratory diseases and affected their well-being.

Diseases that developed as a result of exposure to poisonous gases during the war may take a long time to be noticed, and some veterans may develop disabilities due to the development of these diseases. Therefore, veterans are advised to do medical checkups regularly to ensure the safety of their health. It is the work of the government to provide intervention on how to provide care and treatment to the affected veterans. Healthcare institutions are working hard to make sure the health of the veterans is restored. Government intervention is very crucial when dealing with the issues of the provision of healthcare services to the veterans who had served the war. The government usually provides these services at no cost to improve the health of veterans.

Possible Disabilities from the Gulf War

Many veterans who were involved in the Gulf War experienced symptoms of diseases that later were diagnosed and classified as disabilities. These disabilities stem from the exposure of military personnel to poisonous gases that have been deemed hazardous to human health. The same veterans suffered from the minor effects of vaccines administered to them. The disabilities that a military person may suffer are termed as chronic illnesses, are characterized by numerous symptoms, are often undiagnosed illnesses, and are often infectious diseases. An undiagnosed illness is described by various symptoms that usually manifest without explanation (Institute of Medicine, 2016).

The mentioned symptoms were common to the veterans who served in the Gulf War. Some of the symptoms included menstrual disorders, problems of the skin, cardiovascular symptoms, problems of respiratory systems, fatigue that may cause disturbance of sleep, neurological problems, and the symptoms of gastrointestinal problems (Simms, Watson, & Doebbelling, 2002). The mentioned symptoms are extremely chronic and cause many health problems for veterans. Therefore, these symptoms are known as undiagnosed symptoms and usually cause disabilities to the veteran officers.

The illnesses exhibit multiple symptoms of diseases and disorders including irritable bowel syndrome, fibromyalgia, and chronic fatigue syndrome. These symptoms are usually chronic and lead to the development of disabilities (Simms, Watson, & Doebbelling, 2002). The infectious diseases leading to disabilities among military personnel include visceral leishmaniasis and mycobacterium tuberculosis. These infectious diseases affecting veterans are usually linked with Gulf War service and make affected servicemen inactive and disabled due to hindered or restricted movement. Despite these challenges, the government is usually ready to help the disabled military persons.

Post-traumatic stress disorder. The Canadian forces used a spirituality method to approach soldiers who had PTSD, seeking to define the connection amongst inherent religiousness and divine principles. According to Popoola (2011), Canadian soldiers who had multiple deployments to Afghanistan faced increased levels of PTSD. Trauma linkage and spirituality practice were discovered to have correlations with PTSD during deployment (Popoola, 2011).

According to Ismail et al. (2007), researchers inside the Canadian military came to different conclusions than the authors of a major American report. This Canadian report determined that the mysterious illnesses known as GWS related to many veterans who participated in the Gulf War in 1991, displaying symptoms of chemical toxins rather than anxiety and mental disorders. Approximately 4,500 Canadians took part in the Gulf War, almost 20% of whom had substantial health problems that could be linked to GWS (Ismail et al., 2007). This number is far different than what the United States is reporting among service members suffering from GWS who served during the same time frame as the Canadian service members. Therefore, the coping strategies that Canadian service members used to help with their health issues could be adopted by U.S. leaders to help U.S. service members cope with different physical functioning illnesses.

Iraq and Afghanistan War veterans reporting PTSD. According to Jakupcak et al. (2007), service members who were found to have PTSD had a higher level of anger and hostility when compared to those who had similar past conditions from other wars. Service members who had PTSD showed more anger and aggression than service members who did not show any symptoms of PTSD (Jakupcak et al., 2007). The findings suggested that service members who served in Iraq and Afghanistan should be screened for PTSD and anxiety. According to Engelhard, Arntz, and Hout (2007), concerns have been raised that the survey used for PTSD screening may not distinguish between a person under medical care with PTSD and individuals with additional types of illnesses. Most doctors use a self-reporting scale of PTSD symptoms to determine the level of PTSD a person is suffering. PTSD has been linked to minor stressors and to increased risk of depression and other anxiety disorders.

The increasing role of service members in combat and the related danger of these functions is reflected in data indicating that to date there have been 38,000 service members wounded in action and 2,164 troops killed in action while deployed in support of Operation Enduring Freedom/ Operation Iraqi Freedom (Chaumba & Bride, 2010). Complex levels of stress exposure are linked to higher rates of PTSD (Chaumba & Bride, 2010). Therefore, PTSD could be associated with service members' levels of physical functioning in everyday life (Stretch, Marlowe, & Wright, 1996). Effects of PTSD and role limitations have also been measures by comparing service members who deployed with non-deployed service members (Stretch, Marlowe, & Wright, 1996).

By comparing PTSD's symptom structure between deployed and non-deployed veterans, two models were used to investigate the PTSD symptoms among the GWVs. The symptoms were checked against the PTSD checklist, using the PCL-5 model and the Simm's model. The first model addressed re-experiencing, avoidance, numbing of emotions, and factors leading to hyperarousal among GWVs (Simms & Watson, 2002). The second model targeted re-experiencing, circumvention, dysphoria, and hyperarousal amongst GWVs (Simms & Watson, 2002). The main view of the investigation was to discover which model suited the two groups of veterans. The two groups were then compared using a factor analysis for multi-group confirmatory. The non-deployed group had an adequate model fit that showed no difference between the PCL-5 model and the Simms model (Simms & Watson, 2002). The deployed team had a better fitting model that was consistent with the Simms model (Simms & Watson, 2002). The testing showed that there were differences between the deployed service members and non-deployed service member groups as well as a few similarities in aspects to PTSD severity.

Engdahl, Elhai, Richardson, and Frueh (2011) concluded that military individuals who were deployed to combat zones had more symptoms of PTSD than service members who were not deployed. Symptoms experienced by service members who served in a military war may vary from other types of traumatic incidents because deployment is characterized by continuous threat of risk (Suris & North, 2011). Service members who experienced a greater rate of recurrent traumatic events during military operations also experienced more severe stress problems (Suris & North, 2011). Another source of PTSD for service members was witnessing killings or willfully killing other human beings themselves while in hostile areas (Suris & North, 2011).

There are several approaches to the primary prevention of PTSD in the military. Many studies by the VA have involved data collection from clinical research and hospitals as well as data gathered from surveys of combat troops who served in the Gulf War. Therefore, the information that the VA can gather can be used to find the most efficient treatment opportunities for those diagnosed with PTSD (Hourani, Council, Hubal, & Strange, 2011). The costs incurred by the U.S. military research for PTSD and other psychological disorders connected with the wars in Iraq and Afghanistan are significant not only for armed service members and their families but also for deployment readiness and the community as a whole.

Service members with mental disorders are at risk for other PTSD diagnoses such as drug dependencies, family abuse, and advanced rates of unhealthy medical conditions. Although it may take time for people who suffer from PTSD to feel benefits from therapy or medications, treatment can be effective if patients follow their therapists' plans. One of the methods used by therapists is talk therapy, which usually lasts three to four months before moving the patient to prolonged exposure (PE) therapy. In PE, the therapist exposes the patient to the thoughts, feelings, and situations that the patient had been avoiding. Facing them can help patients learn to cope with the trauma instead of avoiding it. Therapists remind patients not to self-medicate themselves with alcohol or drugs.

Vietnam veterans had higher incidents of PTSD and mortality when compared to GWVs. Vietnam veterans were also more likely to reports illnesses, hospitalizations, medication use, and physical disabilities (Hourani et al., 2011). Their complaints called attention to the relationships between PTSD and physical functioning and mortality, inviting additional study into the area. Litz, Keane, Fisher, Marx, and Monaco (1992) found that

Vietnam veterans with PTSD reported more physical health complaints with the grievances being significantly related to the severity of PTSD symptomatology. Since then, some studies have examined PTSD as a factor contributing to poorer physical health in combat veterans.

Two studies by the VA and the DoD evaluated the potential relationship between PTSD and impairment in physical functioning. Mellman, Kulick-Bell, Ashlock, and Nolan (1995) found that combat veterans with PTSD had poorer sleep habits than combat veterans without PTSD and had poorer sleep habits than a sample of civilians who had not been exposed to combat. A more sensitive indicator of health problems investigated was chemical agents believed to be used by Iraqi leaders during the Gulf War.

Service Members' Deployment

In 1990, the independent nation of Kuwait was invaded by Iraq. The United States began deploying its troops within the first five days of the war (Simms et al., 2002). Approximately 41 countries decided to support the United States by deploying their troops to Kuwait, the goal of ending the Gulf War. From August 1990, troops settled into the region, ready to fight. In January of 1991, intensive air battles against the Iraqi forces began. The following month, ground attacks were at their climax. Fighting was continuous, and within the next four days, the Iraqi troops' resistance began to decline. The decline in troop numbers was rapid. By June of 1992, U.S. troops who took part in this fight had already returned to their home grounds. After the end of the war, the veterans who had survived the fight returned to their homes and resumed normal duties. However, within a short, specified period, these troops began to develop health problems.

Radford (2007) examined stress and depression in combat veterans with physical restrictions and found that mental disorders were the only crucial link between self-reported physical symptoms and stress in deployed veterans. Compared to stress veterans without chronic pain, stress veterans with higher levels of chronic pain had significantly greater scores on the Minnesota Multiphasic Personality-2 (MMPI-2) test, the most widely used and researched standardized psychometric test of adult personality and psychopathology.

Military deployment is a difficult assignment that adversely influences military service members, their families, and their role functioning. Deployment is the movement of service members outside parts of military bases, the relocating of soldiers into zones for war, and the relocation of equipment and soldiers to anticipated regions of military exercises. Deployment has been known as an origin of permanent distress for military personnel and their families (Radford, 2007). Although the National Center for PTSD (2007) listed war trauma, battle fatigue, injury, observing death and stress, and living under extreme conditions as the kinds of distress that were common to service members, other investigators added blasts, injury, and observing death to the list of signs of battle distress. Therefore, deployment stressors and environmentally induced stress were used to illustrate the types of stress experienced by service members. Each type of stress is explained below, highlighting its prevalence among service members (Chaumba & Bride, 2010).

Military Deployment and its Stress on Marriages and Families of Soldiers

The military has programs to help service members cope with the stresses of military life and family. Due to the current military environment, more extensive research is needed regarding the strategies and programs that can aid service members in managing the stresses brought about by being deployed to war and then returning home to marriages and families (Kotlowski, 2009). Hisle-Gorman et al. (2015) noted that "children of deployed and combat-injured service members have more post-deployment visits for mental health treatment, injuries, and child abuse" (p. 247–248) compared to children of service members who have had fewer deployments or family relocation to other military bases (Khaylis, Polusny, Erbes, Gewirtz, & Rath, 2011).

In traditional military practices, military leaders acknowledged that the war experience might create stress for service members, offering all service members a formal psychological debriefing at the end of their deployment (Kotlowski, 2009). According to the DoD (2008), family members face challenges when a service member is deployed. The emotional cycle of service members leaving their families begins with the announcement of deployment and leads to fear of losing a family member.

As departure grows closer for service members, a period of detachment and withdrawal may occur in family members. Therefore, withdrawal may occur to prepare the family for the service member's deployment. Family trauma response has been theorized both as a quality of families and as a dynamic process or path that a family takes when a member is leaving. According to Kotlowski (2009) and the DoD (2008), deployment relates to families either when the service members leave or return from a deployment. Adjustment can lead to stress for and resiliency from family members as parents try to reestablish routines before the service members deploy.

Pierce (2005) noted that military deployments included an extraordinary amount of U.S. military women serving in the major combat positions throughout the region, with numbers extending beyond 33,000. A study was conducted on two groups of Air Force women who were deployed and not deployed to the Persian Gulf. The study findings showed that the Air Force women who were deployed to the Persian Gulf had lengthy and significant illnesses. Although military medical leaders studied the health effects on service members, little study was devoted to the well-being and welfare of females who served in unique numbers and different roles in a combat zone (Pierce, 2005). Pierce (2005) also stated that deployment stressors might impact females differently than males. Nearly three quarters (74%) of female Vietnam veterans reported the jeopardy of bodily harm or death as one of the wartime stressors they experienced (Kimerling, Clum, & Wolfe, 2000). The National Survey of Veterans reported that approximately 24% of female veterans, versus 37% of male veterans, had been exposed to death, illnesses, or distressed people (U.S. Department of Veterans Affairs, 2010).

Agent Exposure

Chemical Agent or Biological Agents' Effects on Role Functioning

The U.S. bombing in Iraq during the Gulf War released a poisonous gas composed of sarin that affected the health of the American veterans in Saudi Arabia during the war. The major bombing took place in January of 1991 in Khamisiya and Nasiriyah. These bombings distributed sarin in the form of cloud dust in the air, with wind carrying this toxic cloud to the other parts of the region, including Saudi Arabia (Orcutt, Erickson, & Wolfe, 2004). According to the research studies conducted by the DoD, the gas plumes were the main cause of the Gulf War illnesses (Orcutt, Erickson, & Wolfe, 2004). It was clear that most GWVs had developed problems in their health that were related to their exposure to this poisonous gas. These exposures happened when the soldiers were not protected from direct contact with these gases (Orcutt, Erickson, & Wolfe, 2004).

Another agent exposure that military personnel may have faced came from direct attacks from either bombing or gunshots. Chemicals released at the explosion sites would be harmful, causing respiratory disease infections after the inhalation of the poisonous gases. The effects may have taken time to manifest, but would cause harm to the health of exposed veterans (Kang et al., 2000). Exposure to and direct contact with chemicals may lead to several health-related problems. Gunshot exposure may result in death or deformities of the troops facing the problem. The majority of the service men in battles in the region would face these problems, especially when enemies invaded their territory (Kang et al., 2000).

The degree of stress the Gulf War service members experienced and the need for adequate answers drives the need to review the many chemical agents to which the military personnel were exposed. Two decades after the Gulf War, GWVs who served during that war have continuously reported symptomatic illnesses at higher rates than service members who did not participate in combat during the Gulf War (Kang et al., 2000). GWVs suffer illnesses that include a mixture of lingering headaches, widespread pain, problems with concentration, memory difficulties, gastrointestinal problems, insistent exhaustion, mood disturbance, and skin abnormalities. The symptoms and difficulties are collectively referred to as GWS (Kang et al., 2000).

Exposure to chemicals (Chong, 2008) and exposure to hazardous substances such as black smoke from hot oil well fires, toxic gas agents, and various vaccines have seemed to add to the progression of GWS between service members (Steele et al., 2012). The Gulf War's anthrax vaccine program involved the inoculation of at least 150,000 American troops with a vaccine of questionable safety in a program that was subsequently criticized for its secrecy, inconsistency, and violations of established ethical principles. Trauma and extreme psychological and physical stress are also noted as significant risk factors for GWS and as contributors to service members' health issues as a result of serving in the Gulf War (Abouzeid et al., 2012).

Reports also indicated that the various exposures associated with Gulf War service are highly inter-correlated (Cherry et al., 2001). Cherry et al. (2001) conducted their study on the complex factors related to the etiology of GWS, concluding that the most significant factors influencing the GWS as regards service members' exposures were the use of pesticides and PB pills (Steele et al., 2012). Further conclusions and generalizations regarding GWS have very complex, multi-factorial etiologies, often involving various deployment-related exposures and the prevalence of factors may vary depending on the identifiable veteran subgroups in the research.

Airborne Pathogens

In this section, the researcher reviews a comparative analysis of mutagenic activities of air samples collected from Riyadh, Saudi Arabia, before, during, and after the Gulf War. According to Al-Khodairy, Al-Dakan, Akel, and Hannan (1998), samples of air quality in Riyadh in 1988 indicated little metabolic activation. After the oil wells of Kuwait had been set on fire, the air quality level changed to high levels of metabolic activation in some cities (Al-Khodairy et al., 1998). Service members may have been affected by a chemical cocktail of mixtures consisting of depleted uranium, pesticides, low-level sarin, PB, multiple vaccines, fuel vapors, exhaust fumes, and chemical agent-resistant coating.

According to Radford (2007), the research study was conducted with other federal agencies on firefighters working in oil wells in Kuwait City in 1991, testing samples of blood for toxic organic chemicals linked with samples from a collection of citizens residing in the United States. The average concentration of volatile organic compounds among the firefighters from Kuwait City was higher. However, among the non-firefighting workers, levels of volatile organic compounds volumes were equal to or lower than the levels found among the citizens living in the United States. Another blood test study was conducted with service members at three different points in time: before, during, and after their deployment to Kuwait. The results of the study showed that tetrachloroethylene, a complex chemical found in degreasing agents used to clean equipment, was the only volatile organic compounds found to be elevated in service members (Radford,2007).

According to Al-Khodairy et al. (1998) and Radford (2007), oil well fires in Kuwait City could have impacted service members who served in the Gulf War. The enforced use of experimental drugs to service members during the Gulf War is challenging in its conflict to government principles codes and the association between investigational drugs and GWS. Beyond its ethical and safety allegations, the vaccine history of the Gulf War is even more alarming when contrasted with developments in the 1990s. In September of 1993, no relevant study of vaccines of any sort regarding GWS had been completed and published by DoD. According to Riegle's office, a report on health consequences of the Gulf War was released, containing a huge body of evidence regarding GWS and possible exposure to chemical and biological agents (McAllister, 1993).

Social Well-being

Social well-being is an indicator used to measure a person's sense of belonging or social attachment (Steele,2015). GWVs were exposed to stressful conditions and changes in lifestyle during their time in the Gulf War. According to Steele (2015), a high level of well-being meant that an individual's condition was positive, while a low level well-being was related to negative activities. For example, when GWVs experienced the invasion of Iraq during the wars and the deaths of their colleagues, their social well-being is highly interfered with during that time. Veterans usually live lives full of difficulties. Veterans' happiness is usually cut short when they experience invasions and the deaths of their friends. Veterans usually live stressful social lives as well. While at war, the interactions between veterans and their families can be strained, with veterans missing their friends and relatives at home (Steele, 2015). These findings demonstrated how veterans suffer from problems connected with their social well-being. Families may even break up when veterans are away from their homes.

When veterans returned to their homes, some of them found it difficult to reconnect with their families and friends. Therefore, veterans suffered from a lack of support from their relatives, which impacted their social well-being. Family care and support are of great importance in terms of improving social well-being. Close contact and interaction with friends can improve a person's social being.

Stress Factors

Psychological Disorders

The majority of GWVs suffered from stress and psychological disorders (Zoroya, 2012). Almost three-quarters of the veterans reported cases of suffering from chronic psychiatric symptoms. Research by DoD to investigate the effects of Gulf War have shown that some participants of the war had developed psychiatric disorders (Zoroya, 2012). Most of the symptoms associated with such disorders occurred unnoticed for the majority of the veterans. Despite this, investigations of patients who had PTSD showed that a small percentage of GWVs will suffer from this disorder. Stress has adverse effects on the well-being of the veterans.

In a war environment, where bombing and shootings are taking place, stress plays a critical role when defining the psychological conditions of a person. Seeing colleagues die brings stress to the life of a veteran (Steele, 2015). Exposure to chemicals especially the sarin chemicals influenced the occurrence of psychological problems to the service members (Steele, 2015).

Family Issues

Another type of stress experienced by service members is family and war. According to Taft, Schumm, Panuzio, and Proctor (2008), battlefield operations place substantial stress on armed forces families, with returning service members frequently reporting problems in re-adjusting to their family home lives after they return as being of primary concern. Research has shown less family interconnectedness, increased numbers of marriages suffering from emotional problems, more frequently reported hopelessness, and spikes in adolescent behavior problems occurring within families as a result of deployments (Taft et al., 2008). Evidence from studies of service members suggests that combat deployment presents a danger to marriage and relationships and creates insecurity for deployed service members (Taft et al., 2008). Researchers have repeatedly suggested that the warning signs of PTSD account for these connections (Taft et al., 2008).

The findings by Taft et al. (2008) concerning stress and depression severity and self-reported physical functioning are inconsistent with previous studies that found more frequent diagnoses of major depression among deployed families (McFarlane, Atchinson, Rafalowicz, & Papay, 1994). This question escalates the degree to which depression severity is related to poorer physical functioning. A study that examined depression severity in comparison to physical functioning would help to clarify the connection between stress, depression, and deployment.

Wright (2009) presented how the Afghan war affected the short and long-term societal, financial, and emotional happiness of service members' families. Throughout peacetime, families of military service members become reasonably accustomed to the numerous moves and other eccentricities of military life, particularly when there is an integral and steady family formation. Investigation of children and families of military service members deployed through Operation Desert Storm verified a surge in depression signs and grief in children (Wright, 2009).

Children exposed to war through a parent's involvement showed variations of stressors and can progress both temporarily and permanently into PTSD. Wright (2009), pointed out common symptoms of children suffering from PTSD reactions as a result of parents' service in war or as a result of being exposed to war trauma. Wright (2009) examined the independent correlation connecting exposure to war ordeal through a family member's psychological health conditions. An experience of war impacts both children and parents, whose emotional reactions are interconnected with one another.

Researchers have addressed the issue of adolescent well-being among Washington state military families. A 2011 research study was conducted by Washington State Juvenile services in order to investigate the relationship between parental military service and juvenile well-being (Reed, Bell, & Edwards, 2011). Data were collected from the 2008 Washington State Youth Survey in public schools, mainly in grades 8-11. The researchers investigated the individual's moods, suicidal thoughts, and quality of life (Reed et al., 2011). The study showed that juveniles in the eighth grade had higher rates of suicidal thoughts, while minors in the ninth, tenth and, twelfth grades had a lower outlooks regarding quality of life (Reed et al., 2011). The study involved all teenage children of deployed service members. There were no programs developed to help military families deal with the situations (Reed et al., 2011).

Economic State

In the United States, the VA supports the success of economic of veterans and their families by bringing communities together to coordinate efforts to improve the welfare of veterans. The agency also provides skills and training to help veterans beyond their military careers. The veterans are well paid to support their families.

Service members often have families and children who require financial support from them (Sutker, Davis, Uddo, & Ditta, 2014). Therefore, the work of the government is to provide those service members with adequate salaries for providing for themselves and their families. Service members are usually given retirement benefits after completing 20 years of military service. They usually receive awards and honorable discharges as a form of appreciation for their service of their country. Because service members play an important role in maintaining the peace and order of their country, they are compensated for their work at levels designed to improve their economic status. However, some service members have waited 10-20 years before receiving service connection awards (Sutker et al., 2014).

Evaluation of Empirical Findings

The Effects of GWS on Service Members and Families

The Gulf War resulted in 776 wounded and injured U.S. service members (Silverleib, 2012). Of the 776 service members wounded in Iraq, 34% were in the 18-25 age range (Silverleib, 2012). The Gulf War resulted in approximately 11.2% of the wounded or injured service members having the potential for experiencing GWS (Silverleib, 2012; RAND Health Care, 2012). The possibility is strong that doctors might diagnose not only the wounded or injured service members, but also all soldiers who experienced combat, with GWS. A strong connection exists between individuals with PTSD and increased rates of suicide. Suicidal tendencies affect both the individual and the individual's family.

According to Zoroya (2012), the U.S. Army reported the highest rate of suicides in July of 2012. The emotional transformation for service members with GWS and PTSD becomes a struggle between life and death. Leaders at the VA confirmed the theory of emotional adjustment issues with a study of 72 service members returning from combat to Fort Carson, Colo. The study revealed that 33 of the 72 service members had attempted suicide to end the emotional distress caused by psychological disorders and PTSD (Zoroya, 2012). Stress factors included family dynamics and the effects of military marriage and divorce.

Effects on Marriage

PTSD impacts the ways that married individuals communicate with one another and can influence psychological well-being. Overall, PTSD can hurt entire households. Compared to veterans without PTSD, veterans with PTSD reported additional troubles in their marriages and communicated fewer feelings and thoughts to their spouses (Jordan et al., 1992). Sexual difficulties also tended to be greater among combat veterans with PTSD. In addition, combat veterans and their partners reported having more difficulty with these sexual issues. Decreased sexual attentiveness may also lead to lower gratification levels within the marriages.

The National Vietnam Veterans Readjustment Study compared veterans with PTSD to those without PTSD. The results indicated that Vietnam veterans with PTSD had divorce rates that were two times higher than Vietnam veterans without PTSD. They also tended to have shorter relationships (Jordan et al., 1992). These symptoms were not restricted to males. Female partners of male veterans with PTSD also reported lower well-being and more social isolation (Jordan et al., 1992).

Efforts Toward the Elimination of Gulf War Syndrome

The VA pays disability compensation to veterans for service-related or service-connected injuries during their military service. Service members must have been released under honorable conditions in order to qualify. According to the VA (2010), disability compensation is used to reimburse service members who have a service-connected disability. The benefits are tax free. Service members who served in the Gulf War can register with the Department of Veterans Gulf War registry. Service members can get free examinations to determine if they have any symptoms related to an undiagnosed illness.

According to the VA (2010), service members had until December 31, 2011, to file claims for the GWS disability. The Veteran Act of Persian Gulf War provided veterans with assistance in filing claims and registering their names on the Gulf War registry. Public Law 105-277 authorized the VA to reward veterans of the Gulf War for health problems or medical conditions that are regulated by VA guidelines, permitting an assumption of military disability. The guidelines stipulated determinations based on contact with toxic agents, diagnoses of PTSD, physical limitation, health problems, wartime hazards, or preventive medications and vaccines related to GWS.

Batten and Pollack (2008) argued that service members who served in the Gulf War and showed signs of ill health should receive care-based treatment based on scientific evidence produced from research and medical evidence. Batten and Pollack (2008) believed that service members who showed symptoms of one or more undiagnosed illnesses would be better served under an incorporated care model. The goal of the incorporated care model would be to provide service members with immediate health care and integration into community programs that would help them with PTSD, anxiety, family and marriage problems, and access to top-tier medical care. The development of rehabilitation program for Gulf War veteran is longer and slower because of the many bureaucratic policies involved in providing medical service to GWVs.

Methodological Review

Methods related to qualitative research include interviewing, applicant observation, research, and analysis documents. For this study, the researcher used a quantitative approach involving the collection of information on participants through survey methods. The use of survey questionnaires enabled the researcher to assemble a huge quantity of numbers within a short time frame. Through surveying, the researcher asked questions related to hypotheses, asking participants to answer specific response categories that were then assigned a numerical value. The numerical values were cataloged in a database and the survey questions were used to create subscales that tested the hypotheses of the study using statistical inference.

Summary

In this literature review, the researcher presented the variety of explanations that have been suggested for the adverse health changes that occurred in GWVs upon their return home. A handful of syndromes and illnesses were identified, including exposure to environmental hazards, PTSD, chemical agent exposure, psychological stress, and substance intake, all of which can lead to difficulties with physical functioning and role functioning. The most common physical symptoms reported by GWVs included fatigue, headaches, rash and dermatitis, joint pain, and memory loss. The external factors capable of inducing these symptoms – pesticides, neurotoxicants, and products of combustion, along with other possible yet unconfirmed sources like chemical warfare agents – were also concluded to have played a part in the development of GWS among veterans.

The problems that the Vietnam veterans encountered were also taken into consideration due to inevitable comparisons with the post-Gulf War health concerns. Despite the studies that have been conducted on GWV health issues, no objective measurement as to the degree of environmental exposure or particular signs of underlying illness has been made. The GWS causes have continuously been elusive as well, requiring continued research.

Future research should be conducted with the goal of improving the welfare of veterans. The government should be accountable and take responsibility for ensuring that veterans' lives are improved, both economically and physically. In Chapter 3, the researcher presents details regarding study methodology, data collection, and instrumentation. The chapter also includes recommendations for appropriate responses to the problem.

CHAPTER 3

Research Methods

In Chapter 2, the researcher offered an analysis of the research related toGWS, stress, PTSD, and the vaccines used by the military, examining them from both historical and current research perspectives. In Chapter 3, the researcher describes the study design methodology, research, data collection, and sampling population. In this study, the researcher examined physical problems experienced by veterans as a result of serving in the Persian Gulf region and that may have influenced their mental well-being, societal functioning, and role limitations. The military population that served in the Gulf War thus acts as a benchmark for identifying undiagnosed illnesses of service members who served in the Gulf War.

The researcher aimed to observe the health symptoms and medical problems experienced by veterans who participated in the Gulf War and to test whether agent exposure and other conflict-related disability factors were related to the physical functioning issues, social and emotional well-being, and role limitations of veterans. Exploring how GWS is related to service members' lives will serve to clarify the importance of Gulf War-related health issues.

Research Method

According to Cooper and Schindler (2011), qualitative research methods are more suitable for investigative styles of research. Such investigative research includes conditions in which variables are unknown. Methods related to qualitative research include interviewing, observation, research, and the analysis of documents. For this study, the researcher used a quantitative approach, employing survey methods to collect information on participants. The use of survey questionnaires enabled the researcher to assemble a significant quantity of statistics within a short time frame. Participants responded to questions related to the study hypotheses, providing response categories that were then assigned with numerical values. These numerical values were cataloged in a database. The survey questions were used to create subscales that tested the hypotheses of the study using statistical inference.

The objective of the research was to investigate whether GWVs exhibited effects on social functioning, emotional well-being, and role limitations upon returning home from the Gulf War. Through quantitative studies, researchers seek to determine relationships and make predictions for use in generalizing findings. With qualitative studies, on the other hand, researchers seek to illuminate, understand, and extrapolate to similar situations (Creswell, 2007). Through this study, the researcher collected data to generate ideas for and awareness of service members who suffer from undiagnosed illnesses.

Research Design

In quantitative studies, researchers seek to make inferences about variable characteristics using measurements or observations and to investigate the results as they apply to the population of concern (Newman & Covrig, 2013). According to Neumann and Robson (2012), quantitative research follows a linear path of defined steps that occur in sequence, with each step leading to the next. The process begins with the researcher creating research questions that direct the plans for design, analysis, sampling, measurement, and data collection. In the social sciences, surveys provide the most effective method of generating and collecting pertinent data, particularly the type used to describe a population that is too large for direct observation. In quantitative research, a researcher uses statistical processes or other means of quantifying data to determine predictions and generalize the findings (Silvia, 2012). For this study, the researcher used a correlational approach.

In conducting correlational researcher, Fields (2013) explained that researchers may observe what naturally goes on in the world without directly interfering with it. In experimental research, researchers manipulate one variable in order to see its effect on another. In a correlational study, the researcher can measure variables at a single point in time or can measure variables repeatedly on multiple occasions. For this study, the researcher used a quantitative, correlational, non-experimental approach to investigate the correlation between agent exposures and disabilities with physical functioning. The researcher also explored the link between exposures, disabilities, physical function, and other measures of veteran well-being such as social, emotional, and role functioning. By using several variables, the researcher used a multiple linear regression to express the relationships between more than one dependent variable and more than one independent variable when observing the data.

Experimental Design

An experimental design is the strongest quantitative design, permitting researchers to isolate researcher manipulation as a strong causal effect on an outcome of interest. The classical experiment has four components: (a) comparison groups, (b) control over the introduction of an intervention, (c) a pretest and a posttest to isolate time order, and (d) randomization of participants into comparison groups to approximate equivalence (Chor, 2010). Though still vulnerable to contamination, the experimental design has the highest degree of internal validity and can allow researchers to be confident in making causal claims.

Quasi-Experimental Design

A quasi-experimental design is not as strong a design as the experimental design because it lacks all four components that characterize experimental design. A quasi-experimental design is usually defined as similar to an experimental design, but lacking a control over the introduction of an intervention and/or a randomization of assignment of participants to comparison groups. Most quasi-experiments will still employ the use of comparison groups and pretest/posttest procedures for isolating between and within group differences. However, the internal validity of these designs will not be as strong as an the internal validity of experimental designs. Causal claims should not be made when employing these types of designs.

Non-Experimental Quantitative Correlational Design

For this study on the impact of GWS, the researcher used a non-experimental research design. The researcher chose to employ this approach in light of the variables of interest that could not be manipulated by sexual characteristics, economic status, social status, or any personal characteristics (Field, 2013). In non-experimental studies, researchers are less certain that outcome differences are due to the independent variable under investigation (Field, 2013). The variables under study in this case were physical functioning, role functioning, emotional functioning, and social functioning.

While some variables are characteristically categorical or quantitative, others may be defined in either way. Therefore, physical functioning was used as an independent variable and dependent variable. Non-experimental research is typically referred to as correlational research or survey research. The classification of a study as correlational research reflects the study strategy more than the research design. The term survey research defines a technique for collecting information (Field, 2013).

Non-experimental research indicates the collection of data without experimental design characteristics in min (e.g., comparison or pre/post). In non-experimental research, the variables under study are not influenced by the investigator and are studied as they occur. For instance, a researcher should not randomly place persons into diverse groups based on knowledge style or gender since these are naturally present characteristics. Quantitative correlation research is a type of non-experimental design that employs material characterized by numbers, uses numbers to measure qualities, and analyzes associations between groups (Chor, 2010). Correlation analysis refers to a statistical approach that determines whether there are substantial positive or negative linear relationships between or among two or more variables (Burns & Grove, 2005).

Cross-Sectional Design

According to Trochim (2006), a cross-sectional research design involves observing individuals who vary in one key quality, such as gender. Therefore, the researcher cannot establish whether any of the independent variables came before the dependent variables in time order. The cross-sectional researcher, then, uses no experimental process, so no variables are manipulated. Correlational designs can be and often are cross-sectional designs. The main purpose of this quantitative, correlational study was to examine the health impact and well-being of service members who served in the Gulf War and to explore the variables, hypothesis testing, and comparisons of the responses of service members who served in the Gulf War between August 1990 and January 1992.

The process of conducting social science research follows one of two methods: quantitative or qualitative. Research design introduces readers to the rationale and purpose of the survey. In quantitative studies, the purpose of the design is to enable the researcher to generalize from a sample population to make inferences about variable characteristics using measurement or observation (Newman & Covrig, 2013). The design justification also must highlight the reasons that the researcher preferred a certain method of data collection. The use of survey questionnaires for this study enabled the researcher to collect a large amount of data within a short time frame. The researcher also had the advantage of identifying a suitable sample from a large population of post-Gulf War veterans.

Correlation analysis defines whether a substantial positive or negative linear relationship exists between two or more variables (Burns & Grove, 2005). The quantitative method explores the why and how of situations based on small and focused samples. Based on the data collected, new ideas and ways to create greater awareness of service members who suffer from undiagnosed illnesses may result. To effectively facilitate a comparison of the two independent variables and their effect on the dependent variable, a multiple liner regression analysis was performed to determine which subscales of each of the independent variables had the largest effect on the well-being of service members.

Recognizing the consequences of each of the independent variable subscales on the health status of veterans generated increased understanding of the impact of the Gulf War on the health status of GWVs. A quantitative study was conducted since the measures for the variables were numerical in content, thereby permitting the quantification of the outcomes and facilitating data analysis using statistical tests. Statistical tests were used to answer the hypotheses and research questions, confirming that the research was based on numerical results and that any insights gained were impartial and correct enough to satisfy the research issues of the study. Furthermore, assumptions drawn from quantitative research were based on equal measures of statistical studies, which served to decrease the influence of researcher partiality.

When experimental designs are premature, impractical, or impossible, researchers must rely on statistical methods to adjust for potentially confounding effects (Cooper & Schindler, 2002). The goal of a correlational study is to search for the relationships among variables based on correlational evidence with some risk issues. There may be also other factors that are associated with the exposure and effect of the variables. Therefore, researchers need to account for the variables, either through experimental design and before the data gathering, or through statistical analysis after the data gathering process.

Research Questions/Hypotheses

The health and well-being outcomes for this study were broken down into four subscales: physical functioning, social functioning, role limitation, and emotional well-being. These health and well-being subscales were measured using the RAND SF-36 Health Survey. The independent variables were broken down into subscales to determine which components had the largest impact on GWVs.

Quantitative research uses both research questions and hypotheses (Chor, 2010). Research questions and hypotheses contain study variables that the researcher describes or groups in order to measure differences between dependent and independent variables (Chor, 2010). Hypotheses reflect the predictions concerning the possible outcomes of the study. Hypotheses may be stated to clarify the expected study results. Some studies may use a null hypothesis to show that there was no link or association among the variables. In the research questions, the researcher begins by stating independent variables and then dependent variables. The appropriate model begins with the descriptive questions, and the researcher may follow with an inferential question for comparing or relating study variables (Chor, 2010).

Hypothesis development is a procedure that explains the expected outcomes of the research study (Creswell, 2007). Sometimes, but not always, a researcher can convey a hypothesis as existential statements, stating that some specific example of the occurrence under examination has some distinguishing and fundamental clarifications. Both hypotheses and research questions are typically used in experimental research (Creswell, 2007; Silvia, 2012). According to Creswell (2007), a well-crafted hypothesis often suggests the best way to perform the research and provides indications of the research design. Hypotheses reflect the predictions concerning the possible outcomes of the study and may be stated in order to clarify the expected study results. Some studies may use the null hypothesis to show that there was no link or relationship between the variables. Each of the variables is then measured using research instruments that will determine the validity and reliability of the study (Creswell, 2007).

The research questions and hypotheses for the current study were used to observe the relationship between agent exposure during the war and physical, social, emotional, and role functioning for GWVs. According to Cohen (1992), the power of statistical testing determines the probability that a null hypothesis will be rejected if false or determines the probability of finding a statistically significant result among an observed sample. The importance of a power analysis arises from the empirical research of the behavioral and social sciences and continues by formulating and assessing hypothesis that the researcher hopes to discard as reasons for establishing facts about the occurrence under research (Cohen, 1992).

Research Question 1

RQ1 asked: To what extent is chemical agent exposure related to physical functioning for veterans who suffered from GWS when controlling for demographic factors? The researcher formulated the following null and alternative hypotheses in response to this question:

$H1_0$: There is no association between chemical agent exposure and levels of physical functioning for GWS veterans when controlling for demographic factors.

$H1_a$: There is an association between chemical agent exposure and levels of physical functioning for GWS veterans when controlling for demographic factors.

Research Question 2

RQ2 asked: To what extent does the physical functioning of veterans who suffer(ed) from GWS related to their social functioning controlling for demographic issues such as disability? The null and alternative hypotheses below were related to this question.

$H2_0$: There is no association between levels of physical functioning and levels of social functioning for GWS veterans when controlling for demographic factors.

$H2_a$: There is an association between levels of physical functioning and levels of social functioning for GWS veterans when controlling for demographic factors.

Research Question 3

RQ3 asked: To what extent is disability status related to physical functioning for veterans who suffer(ed) from GWS when controlling for demographic factors? The following hypotheses were related to this question:

$H3_0$: There is no association between disability status and levels of physical functioning for GWS veterans controlling for demographic factors.

$H3_a$: There is an association between disability status and levels of physical functioning and levels of GWS veterans when controlling for demographic factors.

Research Question 4

RQ4 asked: To what extent does the physical functioning of veterans who suffered from GWS relate to their role limitations due to physical health problems when controlling demographic factors? The two hypotheses below responded to this question:

$H4_0$: There is no association between levels of physical functioning and levels of role limitations for GWS veterans when controlling for demographic factors.

$H4_a$: There is an association between levels of physical functioning and levels of role limitations for GWS veterans when controlling for demographic factors.

Population

The general study population consisted of male and female members of the U.S. military. The specific population consisted of service members who participated in the Gulf War between August 1990 and January 1992 and were exposed to some unknown agent that has been hypothesized to cause GWS. According to DoD (2010), 297,555 of the 696,842 service members who served in the Gulf War, of which approximately 7% were women, are believed to have some symptom resulting from their service in the Persian Gulf.

Participants were selected from panel groups recruited through Facebook. Participants were required to give their consent for their involvement in the research. Internet questionnaires can commonly be used to complement conventional techniques of collecting survey data (Stieger & Reips, 2010). The segment of the target population that uses the Internet can be surveyed economically and rapidly through Internet surveys, while others were contacted by Facebook Messenger. Increasing established analysis methods presented some direct cost savings for the research.

Sampling Strategy

A researcher must identify characteristics of the population of the study and determine sampling techniques. For the current study, the target population consisted of post-Gulf War service members. Probability sampling provided access to a participant panel of veterans who had an equal probability of being selected at random.

The researcher used closed-ended questions rather than open-ended questions in order to take advantage of the benefits of easier and less expensive analysis and higher response rates. Open-ended questions provide participants with opportunities to explain their varying answers and allow respondents to accurately express thoughts or feelings regarding the survey question (Smyth, Dillman, Christian, & McBride, 2009). The first questions were used for background information and demographics. The second part of the survey was designed to collect data on different illnesses that service members may have experienced during their deployments to the Persian Gulf.

Sample Size Calculation

According to Wilborn (2009) and Carpenter (2014), approximately one in four GWVs developed persistent health problems after their deployments. GWVs who were deployed in combat totaled approximately 697,000. Given these estimates, the target population for this study would be 174,250. Using a simple random sampling calculation with a 5% tolerance for sampling error and a 95% confidence interval, the number of respondents needed for achieving a representative sample totaled 118. To meet the target of 118 participants, the researcher posted surveys to 547 respondents, assuming a response rate of 70% to meet the target.

Power Analysis

A power analysis is an examination of a study sample's ability to maximize the probability of detect a true effect in a population. To ensure that this study was appropriately powered to detect a significant effect in the population if that effect was in fact true, an *a priori* power analysis was conducted using G*Power 3.1.9.2. The power of the test was determined for a linear regression analysis, assuming a moderate effect size of $F^2 = 0.15$, an alpha level of $\alpha = 0.05$, a power level ($1-\beta$ error probability) of = 0.80, and a possible 10 predictors in the model. The results indicated that a total sample size of 118 participants would be needed to detect a significant effect in the population. Given the representative sample calculation and the power analysis, a final study sample of 118 participants would suffice for the purposes of this study. However, due to potential response attrition, the survey was distributed to approximately 550 respondents in order to achieve the necessary study sample.

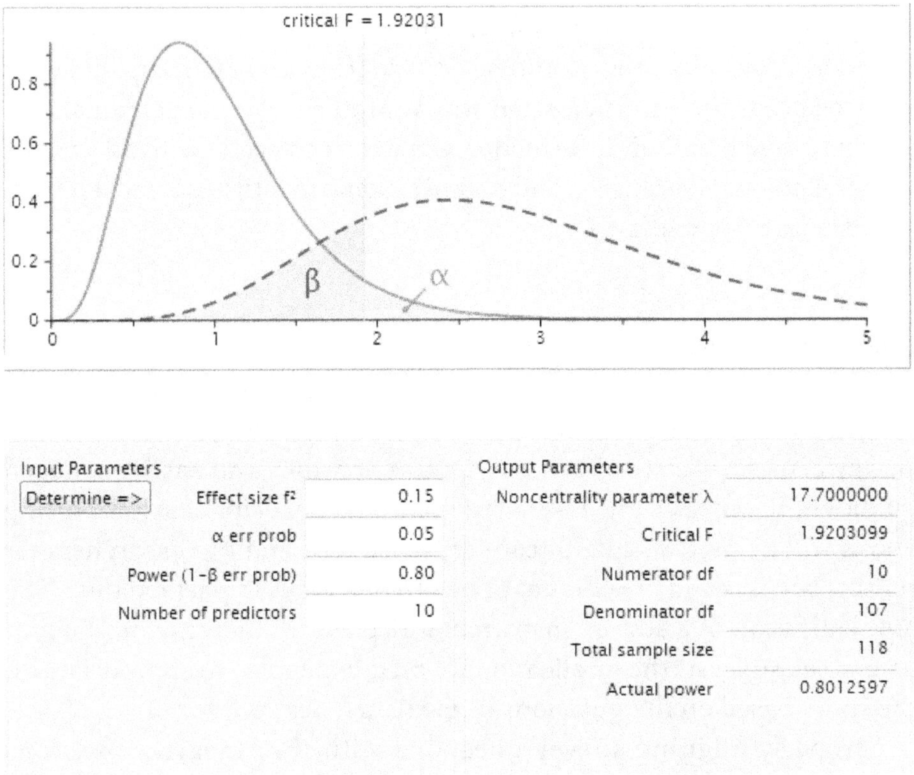

FIGURE 1. G*POWER ANALYSIS.

Informed Consent

Participants were notified through confidentiality agreements that they were free to choose whether to participate or not. Participants were assured of anonymity and informed that their answers would not be singled out and that all individual responses would be kept secret. For the current study, all data resulting from any form of conversation with participants, including email, was considered confidential. All data were stored in a secure locked environment and will be kept for a total of five years after the research was completed.

Confidentiality

Participants were provided with statement of confidentiality, informing them that their identities would remain confidential. Participants were informed that their participation was voluntary. All participants were also informed that their information would be protected, with all specific names, personal identifiers, and organizational identifiers removed from the data (see Appendix C).

Instrumentation

The RAND Health Care 36-item veteran health survey was used to develop survey questions specifically for this study (see Appendix D). The survey consists of a set of general, comprehensible, and easily managed quality-of-life measures. The survey relies on participant self-reporting and is widely used by health care organizations and by researchers for routine surveys and assessment of health outcomes in participants. The authentication of a survey instrument displays an increase of material assembled suggests the implications of certain people are appropriate for the study based on the questions in the data (Creswell, 2009).

Properly aligning survey questions with the research questions was crucial for achieving the desired results (George & Mallery, 2013). According to Salant and Dillman (1994), there are three ways a survey question can be structured – open-ended, closed-ended ordered, and closed-ended unordered. For this study, the researcher used a combination of 36 closed-end ordered questions with three or four options for response. The closed-ended survey questions allowed participants to choose from a pre-existing set of dichotomous answers such as true/false or yes/no, with an option of other.

The advantage of using closed-ended questions is that they are easily analyzed, yield higher response rates, and are less expensive for the researcher. In open-ended questioning, responses do not have options for answers and are provided with the opportunity to explain their responses. The researcher used the first questions to gather background information and demographics, reserving the second part of the survey for collecting data on different illnesses service members may have experienced during their deployment to the Persian Gulf.

Reliability

Reliability means consistency (Coscarelli & Shrock, 2002). A reliable test method involves a comparable outcome that would happen under comparable circumstances. Reliability is an essential property of all assessments. Assessments can be valid even if they are not reliable (Coscarelli & Shrock, 2002). Wollack, Cohen, and Wells (2003), reported that longer tests produced higher reliabilities percentage of measurement error. The percentage of measurement error decreases as the trial length increases. For this study of GWVs, the test consisted of 36 multiple-choice questions. In the study, the construct can be evaluated by validating the finding. This valuation can be proficient by obtaining previous writings validating the tool or by finding validity, where the validity of the device is selected by the investigators in the area the investigation is made-up to measure (Creswell, 2009).

The RAND survey has been found to have strong internal consistency and reliability in multiple studies. Similar findings were observed in other studies that tested this tool on medical outcomes (Ware, 1990). McHorney, Ware, and Raczek (1993) analyzed the RAND 36, finding a strong Cronbach's alpha in multiple subgroups that ranged from 0.78 to 0.93 for all the subscales used in this study, indicating a strong reliability. Cronbach's (1951) alpha was established in order to measure internal consistency, or dependability of a study instrument. Reliability refers to the trustworthiness of an assessment or test and its consistent performance over a period of time. For example, a business might give a survey to staff members in order to measure their work performance. High reliability for that survey would mean that it consistently measured the work performance, while low reliability for that survey would mean that it measured something else or perhaps measured nothing at all. Findings from RAND 36 testing established the RAND survey as a reliable instrument that consistently measures a construct with precision. However, such testing does not establish the instrument's validity or provide a determination regarding whether the device is measuring the actual construct that it was intended to measure.

Validity

Validity pertains to how appropriate the measurement instrument is, as well as how well it measures the variables or concepts in the study (George & Mallery, 2013). The convenience sampling method of data collection will ensure internal validity. The RAND survey was formerly referred to as the Veterans Short Form 36 (SF-36V). The RAND survey is a self-administered patient questionnaire designed to examine health and quality of life. The short-form survey is intended for use in scientific practice research, general population surveys, and health policy evaluations. It is constructed for self-reporting and designed for in-person, phone or Internet administration. The 36-item health survey consists of eight models – emotional problems due to psychological health, general health perceptions, bodily pain, energy vitality, social functioning, physical problems due to physical functioning, and role limitations.

The RAND survey has a high test-retest reliability and validation in general population samples and a variety of disease states administered by researchers. The survey collects data through a variety of means, including surveys, observations, and analysis of existing research findings. All collected data were checked to ensure that information was communicated correctly (George & Mallery, 2013). Doing so ensured that the data collected from the research study of GWS included service members' knowledge, memories, and physical experiences of the reality of the war. Participants were assured they were a part of the entire process and that they played an important role in helping pull the researcher away from any potential bias.

Content Validity

To attain content validity, the researcher must evaluate a known topic in order to assess whether the topic defined is more demanding in content compared to the least sophisticated measure of face validity (Wilson, Pan, & Schumsky, 2012). In a research study, the content validity is used to reveal the information necessary for a specific test or specific subject area. However, in scientific situations, content validity researchers discuss the communication among research elements and the symptom content of a syndrome. Authenticating a health measure or a set of health measures is the process of gathering many diverse kinds of information to decide the most proper understandings of the health score (Stewart et al., 1992). Because health measures can be used for different purposes, validity needs to be assessed independently for each purpose.

Criterion-Related Validity

In the theory and technique of psychological issues, criterion validity is the amount that a quantity is associated with a result. Criterion validity is often divided into concurrent and predictive validity. It refers to an assessment of the portion in question and a conclusion evaluated at the same time, based on the different behavior that must consistently exist in an individual for a diagnosis to be accurately made (Neuman, 2005). Thus, actual, visible data on typical traits are given more status than those that are expected or self-reported.

Construct Validity

Construct validity refers to the degree to which implications can reasonably be made from the operationalization in the study to the speculative constructs on which those operatives were based. Research tests the validity of a measure by correlating it with an already established measure that is a similar concept (Creswell, 2009). McHorney et al. (1993) found that psychometric validity existed using principal component analysis, identifying two factors that accounted for 70% of the shared variance of all items. An overarching physical health factor showed strong correlation that varied from $r = 0.77$ to 1.00 for physical health subscales. Similarly, an overarching mental health factor which that showed strong correlation that varied from $r = 0.62$ to 1.00 for mental health subscales. The same study found the physical functioning ($r = 1.00$) and role physical ($r = 0.71$)

subscales of the RAND 36 to have strong convergent validity with clinical medical health measures. In addition, the mental functioning (r = 1.00), emotional functioning (r = 0.54), and social functioning (r = 0.54) subscales had strong convergent validity with clinical psychiatric disorder measures. These findings established the RAND survey as a valid instrument for measuring the constructs it is intended to measure.

Data Collection

The data for this study was collected using PsychData surveying services. The participants were recruited via selected Facebook panel groups. PsychData narrowed the sample to the desired target population by filtering participants based on exclusion and inclusion criteria. The survey was provided in an online survey format that was distributed to potential participants via secure website.

PsychData maintains a secure online server to ensure that the identity of the participants will be kept confidential when entering their information in the survey. Each participant was prompted in the survey to agree to informed consent before they participate in the study. If participants chose not to consent to taking the survey, they were diverted to a screen that thanked them for their time. Once potential participants agreed to the informed consent terms, they went on to complete a series of exclusion and inclusion criteria questions to aid with screening potential valid participants. If respondents did not meet inclusion or exclusion criteria, they were diverted to a screen that thanked them for their time.

Once a respondent was identified as a valid candidate for the study, he or she was diverted to the survey with a consolidated version of the researcher-created background and demographic questions and the RAND 36-item health questionnaire. The survey took approximately 15-20 minutes to complete. Once participants completed the survey, a window appeared providing the informed consent form along with contact information for the principal researcher and IRB information for them to print and keep for their records. The survey responses for all the participants were collated in a data format suitable for import into a SPSS v24 data file.

All identifying information from data were removed before the data were uploaded by a unique subject number to a secure computer, thereby protecting the confidentiality of participants. Any breach of security was reported to the proper authority. Data remained confidential, with participants' information kept anonymous. After a period of five years, all identifiers and participant information will be destroyed.

Measure of Variables

Description of Variables

A correlational analysis of the four independent variables, physical functioning, social functioning, emotional functioning, role limitations, and their effect on the dependent variable of health issues, was performed to determine which subscales of each of the independent variables had the largest effect on health outcomes in service members who served in the Gulf War. Recognizing the effects of each of the independent variable subscales on physical functioning which helps the understanding of how health issues related service members. The concept, measurement type, scoring, and operational definition are provided. The four dependent variables identified for this study are listed and described below. Table 1 provides a summary description of the variables that were measured and analyzed for this study.

- Physical functioning is defined as the type and intensity of physical activities that participants are able to engage in.

- Social functioning is defined as those social activities that individuals engage in with friends, family, and social groups.

- Physical role functioning deals with job-related limitations, although many measures also included limitations in the performance of everyday activities.

- Emotional functioning is defined a person's state of mind and behavior.

Table 1. *Study Variables*

Measure	Study variable	Variable type	Scoring	Operational definition
Age	Demo.	Ordinal	4 categories	Age of respondent in years
Gender	Demo.	Nominal	2 categories	Male/female
Race/ethnicity	Demo.	Nominal	5 categories	Caucasian, African-American, Asian, Hispanic, Other
Marital status	Demo.	Nominal	3 categories	Single, Married, Divorced, Separated/Widowed
Socio-economic status	Demo.	Ordinal	5 categories	Household income range
Agent exposure	IV	Interval	Count	Exposure to agents during the Gulf-War (12 categories, see survey in Appendix D)
Disability	IV	Interval	Count	Disabilities that a respondent suffers from due to service (10 categories see survey in Appendix D)
Symptoms	IV	Interval	Count	Symptoms that a respondent suffers from due to service in the military (11 categories see survey in Appendix D)
Physical functioning	IV/DV	Interval	Subscale avg. ranging 0-100	Complex activities; activities considered essential for maintaining independence
Social functioning	DV	Interval	Subscale avg. ranging 0-100	Social activity with friends, family, and social groups
Emotional functioning	DV	Interval	Subscale avg. ranging 0-100	Emotional and behavioral disorders
Physical role functioning	DV	Interval	Subscale avg. ranging 0-100	Limitations in the performance of work

Note: Demo. refers to demographic variables, IV refers to independent variable, and DV refers to dependent variable.

Scoring of RAND 36

According to Ware and Sherbourne (1992), the RAND 36 involves a two-step scoring process procedure. First, the researcher uses a scoring key of numeric value, with all subject matters calculated with the higher number present for an acceptable health status. In the second step, the subject matter in a parallel scale is averaged to produce the subscale score. Subject matter that is left open is not in the count when computing the total score. Therefore, the total number indicates the middle point for all subject matter in the measure to which the participant responded.

Demographics

Demographic variables were selected as controls for the analysis. Age, gender, race/ethnicity, marital status, and socio-economic status were the measured socio-demographic characteristics of the participants. Age indicated each veteran's age in years at the time of the completion of the RAND survey (age 30 to 60-plus). Race/ethnicity was measured by prompting the respondent to self-identify as Caucasian, African-American, Hispanic, Asian, or other race/ethnicity groups. Marital status for this study was given by an indicator variable, with respondents indicating whether they were single, married, divorced, or separated/widowed). Socio-economic status was measured by participants report of their average household incomes from five possible income ranges.

Exposure, Disability, and Symptoms

Three independent variables were identified as having strong theoretical implications for the dependent variables of interest. Exposures were identified as agents (chemical, biological, or otherwise) that the veterans were exposed to during their tour during the Gulf War. Respondents used a list to identify all of the exposures that applied to them and providing a count of the number of exposures. Disability was identified as physical and psychological problems that veterans experienced after their tour in the Gulf War. As with exposures, respondents were presented with a list of disabilities from which they identified those that applied to them and indicated a count measure. Lastly, symptoms were identified as the actual physical symptoms that are associated with GWS and consisted of a list of symptoms from which participants indicate those that applied and provided a count measure.

Data Analysis

For this study, the researcher conducted data analysis after completing the data collection process. The most common quantitative statistics analysis includes the descriptive statistics of standard deviations, means, frequency, and mode. The descriptive statistics determined the service members' health and well-being status after their Gulf War involvement. Inferential statistical tests for hypotheses examination were conducted.

The common initial stages of data analysis involve cleaning and organizing data. The data were screened for duplicates and data collection errors. Variables were coded appropriately, and all continuous variables were tested for assumptions of normality and removal of extreme outliers. All nominal variables were assessed to make sure there were enough cases within each category to properly estimate the variable. Each of the questionnaire items that comprised the subscales for physical, social, emotional, and role functioning were recoded and averaged according to RAND's specifications for the instrument. Reliability tests, using inter-item correlation, were conducted to ensure that each of the subscales had adequate internal consistency. These reliability tests were assessed by using the Cronbach's alpha test statistic with an appropriate cutoff value of 0.70, indicating sufficient internal consistency.

Descriptive Analysis

The purpose of selecting the descriptive data was to review or define the set of quantitative data. For the current study, data were selected to define or illustrate the population or sample being researched. The population for this study consisted of military personnel who served in the military during the Gulf War and who were exposed to agents suspected of causing GWS. The descriptive analyses consisted of frequencies and percentages of the nominal variables – in this case, gender, race, and marital status.

In addition, means and standard deviations were used to examine measures of central tendency for all continuous variables such as age, socio-economic status, agent exposure, disability, symptoms, and each of the averaged subscales for the RAND 36-item questionnaire. These subscales consisted of physical, social, emotional, and role functioning and served as the dependent variables of interest for this analysis.

Inferential Analysis

For the preliminary analyses, paired combinations of the demographic, independent, and dependent variables were conducted using bivariate statistical tests. Preliminary bivariate analyses were conducted to identify interesting relationships prior to the primary analysis and in order to observe whether covariates made relevant contributions to the model. The preliminary bivariate analyses also served to observe whether covariates in a model were overly multi-collinear, causing problems for estimation (Field, 2009). Categorical, or nominal variables, were conducted using Pearson's chi-square test of association cross-tabulation. These cross-tabulation bivariate tests paired different combinations of gender, race/ethnicity, and marital status to observe possible associations.

In addition, the bivariate associations of continuous (interval) variables of age, socio-economic status, agent exposure, disability, symptoms, and RAND Health Care survey subscales were assessed using Pearson's *r* correlation tests. The mean differences of continuous (interval/count) variables by group (categorical variables) were assessed using independent sample t-tests and analysis of variance (ANOVA), since there were likely to be mean differences in socio-economic status by race/ethnicity in the sample. A one-way ANOVA established these mean differences by race/ethnicity category and provided the strength of the effect of race on SES differences. Each of these bivariate tests were assessed to ensure that violations of the assumptions of these tests are not violated, such as normality, homogeneity of variance, and the independence of observations. In the event that these assumptions were violated, appropriate, nonparametric tests were conducted and reported.

A correlation analysis, according to Cooper and Schindler (2011), is best used to determine the degree of relationships and their impact on one another. A linear correlation analysis is considered one of the most appropriate methods for reporting correlates such as those found in this study (Creswell, 2007). Each of the hypotheses for the research questions were tested using ordinary least squares (OLS) linear regression analysis. OLS linear regression allows the researcher to estimate the association between a covariate and an outcome of interest holding all other covariates in the model constant. The association is expressed in terms of a correlation coefficient that yields both the direction and magnitude of the relationship (Field, 2009). In addition, this estimated association can be assessed whether it is statistically different from zero meaning no association is present using a t-statistic and a p-value. Lastly, OLS regression also produces a statistic called R^2, which allows the researcher to identify the overall percentage of variance explained in the outcome variable by the set of covariates being introduced into the model. Each of the dependent variables – physical, social, emotional, and role functioning – were regressed on the covariates to test each of the hypotheses for this study (Field, 2009).

For the primary analyses, the hypotheses for each research question were assessed using OLS multiple linear regression analyses. The demographics and the primary independent variables (agent exposure, disabilities, symptoms) were entered into the model to observe the beta coefficient strength of association and the statistical significance of these associations with each of the RAND 36-item health subscales dependent variables (physical, social, emotional, and role functioning).

The results of these multivariate tests allowed the researcher to accept or reject the null hypotheses for each of the research questions in this study. If the hypothesized relationship was not significantly different from zero, then the null hypothesis was accepted. If the hypothesized relationship was significantly different from zero, then the null hypothesis was rejected and alternate hypothesis was accepted. Lastly, model fit statistics were also assessed. The F-test was also reported, assessing whether the model fits the data, along with the R^2 coefficient that determined the model's contribution towards explaining the dependent variables of interest.

Procedure

In the second portion of the survey, the researcher asked multiple choice and open-ended deployment questions. The questions dealt with: (a) deployment experiences, (b) combat experiences, (c) exposure to chemicals, (d) PTSD, and (e) health-related symptoms that fall under GWS. Injury in the theater of operations was also determined through a question that asked about injuries occurring during deployment and asked for input regarding the nature of the injury (vehicular accident, fragment, bullet, etc.). These questions served as potential predictors of physical, social, emotional and role functioning for deployed service members.

The procedure and specifications of variables were ideal for determining the effect of war deployment on the health and well-being functioning of GWVs. The process also aided in identifying the factors before, during, and after deployment that were associated with poorer physical, social, emotional, and role functioning. The correlation of war deployment on physical, social, emotional, and role function may be influenced by multiple psychosocial, and deployment exposure factors.

Summary

In Chapter 3, the researcher presented the methodology and design of the current study. The researcher determined that a quantitative correlational approach would be the most appropriate design, given the research questions. The study involved a sample of service members who served on active duty between August 1990 and January 1992 and who were assigned to the Persian Gulf during that time frame. The researcher ensured that the study sample was appropriately representative of military veterans, with the sample including appropriate proportions of the various military branches and of both male and female veterans. The sample also included veterans who were exposed to suspected GWS agents.

Chapter 3 also included a discussion of the study population, sample population, data collection procedures, study validity, study reliability, and data analysis procedures. The dependent variable for this study was the health and well-being outcomes of post-Gulf War veterans who served in the Persian Gulf region. These health and well-being outcomes consisted of physical, social, emotional, and role functioning status as measured by the RAND 36-item questionnaire. In Chapter 4, the researcher outlines the results of the data analysis.

CHAPTER 4

Results

Introduction

The purpose of this quantitative, correlational, non-experimental study was to survey the health symptoms and medical problems associated with veterans who participated in the Gulf War. This current study was designed to test whether agent exposure, and other conflict-related disability factors, are related to health issues, social and physiological welfare, and the well-being of veterans. Specifically, the quantitative, correlational non-experimental research examined the correlation between agent exposures and disabilities with the physical functioning of the veteran population. A discussion of the sampling method, field test, and process for collecting and analyzing data were included in Chapter 4, along with the findings of the study. Four major categories emerged that led to answers for the research questions: agent exposure, physical functioning, social functioning, and veterans' well-being. Demographic data from the 118 GWVs who participated in this study provided the descriptive statistics and quantitative contents.

Data Collection

Approval to begin data collection was obtained from the Institutional Review Board of the University of Phoenix in May 2018. Data collection was then performed over a period of two months, beginning in May 2018 and continuing through July 2018, with participant selection initiated on a national scale via social media on Facebook. However, limitations in policies and responsiveness resulted in more follow-up with participant access because of direct personal solicitations, as this researcher had occasion to interact with veterans through Facebook and to remind participants to complete the survey. The data for this study was collected using PsychData surveying services, with participants being directed to the veteran survey from the link. The researcher provided an explanation of the study purposes and provided disclosures a second time on the first page of the veteran survey. Respondents were given the opportunity to elect to participate or not participate in the veteran survey by selecting "yes" or "no" to the consent question on the first page of the veteran survey with the disclosures. The online survey was created on a PsychData account, with a copy of the survey provided in supplemental documents called Veteran Survey v2-3.

Data Analysis

Data were collected through an on-line survey using the Facebook platform. Participants were veterans of the Gulf War. Power analysis indicated that a total of 118 participants would be required in order to reach data saturation, which could be achieved with a 70% response rate among 176 participants. The researcher used a quantitative approach and survey method to collect information on participants. Through the use of survey questionnaires, the researcher was able to assemble a large quantity of data regarding participant characteristics within a short time frame. The data for this study were collected using PsychData surveying services, with data organized, classified, and coded by PsychData and used to assist the researcher in organizing and sorting the data and interpreting the data into topics representations of research questions. Relevant data and coding categories were generated by PsychData to form the basis for theme development and to assist in uncovering symptoms and patterns.

Research Questions

The researcher used a set of questions to guide the research. Per Creswell (2007), the research focused the questions on broad issues that must be addressed in order to adequately understand the everyday phenomena of GWS exposures, disabilities, and physical functioning and how those phenomena impact affect the social, emotional, and role functioning of post-Gulf War veterans. According to Creswell (2007), a thought-out and concentrated research question leads directly into a researcher's hypotheses, which in turn gives insight into the researcher's question.

Demographic factors are personal characteristics used to gather and evaluate data on individuals within a population (Cohen, 1998). Typical factors include age, gender, marital status, race, education, income, and occupation. Cohen (1998) noted that researchers study the demographic makeup of a population in order to determine the growth of communities and shared experiences. For this proposal, the researcher collected demographic data related to age, gender, race/ethnicity, marital status, and socioeconomic status.

Research Question 1

RQ1 asked: To what extent is chemical agent exposure related to physical functioning for veterans who suffered from Gulf War Syndrome when controlling for demographic factors? The following are the null and alternative hypotheses:

$H1_0$: There is no association between chemical agent exposure and levels of physical functioning for GWS veterans when controlling for demographic factors.

$H1_a$: There is an association between chemical agent exposure and levels of physical functioning for GWS veterans when controlling for demographic factors..

Research Question 2

RQ2 asked: To what extent does the physical functioning of veterans who suffer from Gulf War Syndrome relate to their social functioning when controlling for demographic issues such as disability? The null and alternative hypotheses for RQ2 are as follows:

$H2_o$: There is no association between levels of physical functioning and levels of social functioning for GWS veterans when controlling for demographic factors.

$H2_a$: There is an association between levels of physical functioning and levels of social functioning for GWS veterans when controlling for demographic factors.

Research Question 3

RQ3 asked: To what extent is physical functioning related to emotional well-being? The null and alternative hypotheses for this question are as follows:

$H3_o$: There is no relationship of physical functioning to emotional well-being.

$H3_a$: There is a relationship of physical functioning to emotional well-being.

Research Question 4

RQ4 asked: To what extent does the physical functioning of veterans who suffer from Gulf War Syndrome relate to their role limitations due to physical health problems when controlling for demographic factors? The related null and hypotheses are:

$H4_o$: There is no association between levels of physical functioning and levels of role limitations for GWS veterans when controlling for demographic factors.

$H4_a$: There is an association between levels of physical functioning and levels of role limitations for GWS veterans when controlling for demographic factors.

Descriptive Statistics

A summary of the frequencies and percentages for all categorical the sample size was 176 participants for the study variables (see Table 1). Four-fifths of the sample population (80.1%) were male. In terms of age, half of the sample (50.0%) fell within the 50-59 range, with the 40-49 age bracket coming in a close second at 40.9%. In terms of race/ethnicity, the majority of the participants (71.6%) were White/European American, with Black/African American participants making up the second largest group (17.6%). The majority (65.9%) of the sample participants were married, with the next largest group (21.0%) consisting of divorced respondents. In terms of income categories, the sample was evenly split between the $30,001-$50,000 range and the $50,001-$75,000 range, with 22.7% of respondents in each group. In terms of educational level, the largest proportion of participants (45.5%) indicated that they had attended some college, followed by those who earned bachelor's degrees (21.6%). The majority of the sample (55.7%) was VA rated as having a disability, with the next largest category comprised of participants who did not try to get rated (19.3%). Regarding disabilities, 35.8% of participants responded that they were both physically and emotionally disabled, with the next largest group (31.8%) indicating that they were emotionally disabled. Almost three-quarters of the sample (71.0%) indicated that they had not been formally diagnosed with GWS by their physicians but felt that they did have symptoms. The next largest group (14.8%) indicated that they had been diagnosed with GWS by their physicians.

Table 2. *Frequencies and Percentages for Categorical Variables*

The means and standard deviations for the continuous study variables are presented in Table 2. Agent exposure is an environmental and chemical hazard with potential health risks for individuals who had been exposed to chemical and biological agents during their Gulf War experiences. Agent exposure ranged from 0 to 12 and had a mean value of 5.29. Physical functioning ranged from 0 to 100, with higher scores indicating stronger physical functioning. The sample had a mean physical functioning score of 52.59. Social functioning ranged from 0 to 100, with higher scores indicating stronger social functioning and with the sample having a mean of 43.53. Emotional well-being ranged from 0 to 96, with higher scores indicating stronger well-being. The sample had a mean emotional well-being score of 44.50. Role limitations due to physical health ranged from 0 to 100, with higher scores indicating less limitations and the sample having a mean of 29.12. Role limitations due to emotional problems ranged from 0 to 100, with higher scores indicating fewer limitations. The sample had a mean role limitation score of 30.98. A reliability analysis of the items for the RAND 36-Item Health Survey was conducted with a subscale used for the overall participants in this study. The results indicated a very high internal consistency for each subscale, with Cronbach's alphas all exceeding 0.700 and ranging from 0.842 to 0.934. These reliability findings suggested that the measurement of these constructs had excellent precision.

Preliminary Analysis Results

Table 3 reports the means and standard deviations for continuous variables relationship between demographic and gender. The standard deviation is a measure that is used to quantify the amount of variation or dispersion. A greater proportion of white/Caucasian (75.9%) were male, as compared to female participants at 54.3%. A greater proportion of married respondents (73.0%) were male, as compared to those who were female (37.1%). A greater proportion of divorced respondents were female (40.0%) as compared to those divorced respondents who were male (16.3%).): A greater percentage of participants with graduate degrees were female (25.7%) as compared to the 9.2% of respondents with graduate degrees who were male. There was no relationship between GWS diagnosis and gender.

Table 3. *Means and Standard Deviations for Continuous Variables*

Variable	*N*	*M*	*SD*	*Min*	*Max*	*alpha*
Agent exposure count	176	5.29	2.71	0	12	-
Physical functioning mean	176	52.59	28.30	0	100	.934
Social functioning mean	170	43.53	29.46	0	100	-
Emotional well-being mean	168	44.50	22.37	0	96	.842
Role limitations due to physical health	170	29.12	39.29	0	100	.891
Role limitations due to emotional problems	170	30.98	40.64	0	100	.856

Note: *N*s not equal to 176 reflect missing data.

Table 4 provides frequencies and percentages for participant demographics by age categories. A Pearson's square chi-square test of association was conducted to assess whether there was any bivariate relationship between these demographics and age. The only significant association was between whether participants believed that the VA doctors paid attention to them and their age, χ^2 (6) = 15.58, p = 0.016. Of those participants who indicated that VA doctors paid attention to them often, a larger proportion of them were in the 60 years or over age category (43.8%), compared to the 50 to 59 years (14.8%) and 40 to 49 years (11.1%) categories. There was no indication of an association between gender, race/ethnicity, marital status, household income, education, VA rating, disability, or GWS diagnosis with age.

Table 4. *Frequencies and Percentages for Demographic Variables by Gender*

Variable	Male *n*	Male %	Female *n*	Female %	χ^2	*p*
Age					.72	.699
40 to 49 years	58	41.1 [a]	14	40.0 [a]		
50 to 59 years	69	48.9 [a]	19	54.3 [a]		
60 years or over	14	9.9 [a]	2	5.7 [a]		
Race/ethnicity (3 groups)					6.44	.040
White/Caucasian	107	75.9 [a]	19	54.3 [b]		
Black/African American	21	14.9 [a]	10	28.6 [a]		
Other race/ethnicity	13	9.2 [a]	6	17.1 [a]		
Marital status					16.19	.003
Single	9	6.4 [a]	5	14.3 [a]		
Married	103	73.0 [a]	13	37.1 [b]		
Divorced	23	16.3 [a]	14	40.0 [b]		
Separated	4	2.8 [a]	2	5.7 [a]		
Widowed	2	1.4 [a]	1	2.9 [a]		
Annual household income					5.69	.338
Less than $30,000 per year	18	12.8 [a]	7	20.0 [a]		
$30,001 to $50,000 per year	36	25.5 [a]	4	11.4 [a]		
$50,001 to $75,000 per year	31	22.0 [a]	9	25.7 [a]		
$75,001 to $100,000 per year	25	17.7 [a]	9	25.7 [a]		
$100,000 to 125,000 per year	14	9.9 [a]	4	11.4 [a]		
$125,001 or more per year	17	12.1 [a]	2	5.7 [a]		
Education level (4 groups)					10.03	.018
Up to a high school diploma	32	22.7 [a]	4	11.4 [a]		
Some college	68	48.2 [a]	12	34.3 [a]		
Bachelor's degree	28	19.9 [a]	10	28.6 [a]		
Graduate degree	13	9.2 [a]	9	25.7 [b]		
VA rated					8.52	.130
Yes	76	53.9 [a]	22	62.9 [a]		
After years of delay	15	10.6 [a]	3	8.6 [a]		
Rating Denied	10	7.1 [a]	4	11.4 [a]		
Refused to Rate	0	.0 [a]	1	2.9 [b]		
Pending Completion	11	7.8 [a]	0	.0 [a]		
Did Not Try	29	20.6 [a]	5	14.3 [a]		
VA doctors paid attention					2.06	.561
None	31	22.0 [a]	5	14.3 [a]		
Rarely	43	30.5 [a]	10	28.6 [a]		
Occasionally	44	31.2 [a]	15	42.9 [a]		
Often	23	16.3 [a]	5	14.3 [a]		
Physically or emotionally disabled by experience in the Gulf War					5.36	.147
I was physically disabled	17	12.1 [a]	0	.0 [b]		
I was emotionally disabled	43	30.5 [a]	13	37.1 [a]		

I was both physically and emotionally disabled	48	34.0 [a]	15	42.9 [a]		
None of these apply	33	23.4 [a]	7	20.0 [a]		
Gulf War Syndrome diagnosis					1.21	.545
I have been formally diagnosed with Gulf War Syndrome by my physician	21	14.9 [a]	5	14.3 [a]		
I have not been formally diagnosed with GWS, but I do have symptoms of GWS	102	72.3 [a]	23	65.7 [a]		
I have not been diagnosed and I don't have symptoms consistent with GWS	18	12.8 [a]	7	20.0 [a]		

Note. For each row category, pairs of column proportions with different superscripts differed significantly, $p < 0.05$.

Table 5 provides frequencies and percentages for participant demographics by age categories. A Pearson's chi-square test of association was conducted to assess whether there was a bivariate relationship between demographics and age. The only significant association was between whether participants believed that the VA doctors paid attention to them and their age, $\chi^2 (6) = 15.58$, $p = 0.016$. Of those participants who indicated that VA doctors paid attention to them often, a larger proportion of them were in the 60+ age range (43.8%), compared with the 14.8% who were in the 50-59 age range and the 11.1% who were in the 40-49 age range. There was no indication of an association between gender, race/ethnicity, marital status, household income, education, VA rating, disability, or GWS diagnosis with age.

Table 5. *Frequencies and Percentages for Demographic Variables by Age*

	40 to 49 years		50 to 59 years		60 years or over			
Variable	*n*	%	*n*	%	*n*	%	χ^2	*p*
Gender							.72	.699
Male	58	80.6 [a]	69	78.4 [a]	14	87.5 [a]		
Female	14	19.4 [a]	19	21.6 [a]	2	12.5 [a]		
Race/ethnicity (3 groups)							3.02	.555
White/Caucasian	49	68.1 [a]	64	72.7 [a]	13	81.3 [a]		
Black/African American	13	18.1 [a]	17	19.3 [a]	1	6.3 [a]		
Other race/ethnicity	10	13.9 [a]	7	8.0 [a]	2	12.5 [a]		

Marital status							6.70	.570
Single	7	9.7 [a]	7	8.0 [a]	0	.0 [a]		
Married	47	65.3 [a]	55	62.5 [a]	14	87.5 [a]		
Divorced	13	18.1 [a]	22	25.0 [a]	2	12.5 [a]		
Separated	4	5.6 [a]	2	2.3 [a]	0	.0 [a]		
Widowed	1	1.4 [a]	2	2.3 [a]	0	.0 [a]		
Annual household income							3.55	.965
Less than $30,000 per year	11	15.3 [a]	13	14.8 [a]	1	6.3 [a]		
$30,001 to $50,000 per year	16	22.2 [a]	18	20.5 [a]	6	37.5 [a]		
$50,001 to $75,000 per year	17	23.6 [a]	20	22.7 [a]	3	18.8 [a]		
$75,001 to $100,000 per year	12	16.7 [a]	19	21.6 [a]	3	18.8 [a]		
$100,000 to 125,000 per year	8	11.1 [a]	9	10.2 [a]	1	6.3 [a]		
$125,001 or more per year	8	11.1 [a]	9	10.2 [a]	2	12.5 [a]		
Education level (4 groups)							8.01	.237
Up to a high school diploma	18	25.0 [a]	16	18.2 [a]	2	12.5 [a]		
Some college	35	48.6 [a]	38	43.2 [a]	7	43.8 [a]		
Bachelor's degree	10	13.9 [a]	25	28.4 [a]	3	18.8 [a]		
Graduate degree	9	12.5 [a]	9	10.2 [a]	4	25.0 [a]		
VA rated							6.00	.815
Yes	38	52.8 [a]	48	54.5 [a]	12	75.0 [a]		
After years of delay	7	9.7 [a]	10	11.4 [a]	1	6.3 [a]		
Rating Denied	8	11.1 [a]	6	6.8 [a]	0	.0 [a]		
Refused to Rate	0	.0 [a]	1	1.1 [a]	0	.0 [a]		
Pending Completion	5	6.9 [a]	6	6.8 [a]	0	.0 [a]		
Did Not Try	14	19.4 [a]	17	19.3 [a]	3	18.8 [a]		
VA doctors paid attention							15.58	.016
None	16	22.2 [a]	19	21.6 [a]	1	6.3 [a]		
Rarely	27	37.5 [a]	21	23.9 [a]	5	31.3 [a]		
Occasionally	21	29.2 [a]	35	39.8 [a]	3	18.8 [a]		
Often	8	11.1 [a]	13	14.8 [a]	7	43.8 [b]		
Physically or emotionally disabled by experience in the Gulf War							3.62	.728
I was physically disabled (e.g. combat or non-combat wounds)	5	6.9 [a]	9	10.2 [a]	3	18.8 [a]		
I was emotionally disabled (e.g. PTSD or chronic depression)	25	34.7 [a]	25	28.4 [a]	6	37.5 [a]		

I was both physically and emotionally disabled	25	34.7 [a]	33	37.5 [a]	5	31.3 [a]		
None of these apply	17	23.6 [a]	21	23.9 [a]	2	12.5 [a]		
Gulf War Syndrome diagnosis							6.30	.178
I have been formally diagnosed with Gulf War Syndrome by my physician	7	9.7 [a]	17	19.3 [a]	2	12.5 [a]		
I have not been formally diagnosed with GWS, but I do have symptoms of GWS	54	75.0 [a]	57	64.8 [a]	14	87.5 [a]		
I have not been diagnosed and I don't have symptoms consistent with GWS	11	15.3 [a]	14	15.9 [a]	0	.0 [a]		

Note. For each row category, pairs of column proportions with different superscripts differed significantly, $p < 0.05$.

Table 6 provides demographics for race/ethnicity. A greater proportion of participants who selected "other" for race/ethnicity (45.0%) earned less than $30,000 per year, as compared to Black/African American participants (26.3%). There was no relationship between race/ethnicity and being physically or emotionally disabled by experience in the Gulf War.

Table 6. *Frequencies and Percentages for Demographic Variables by Ethnicity*

	White/Caucasian		Black/African		Other Race			
Variable	*n*	%	*n*	%	*n*	%	χ^2	*p*
Gender							6.44	.040
Male	107	84.9 [a]	21	67.7 [a]	13	68.4 [a]		
Female	19	15.1 [a]	10	32.3 [a]	6	31.6 [a]		
Age							3.02	.555
40 to 49 years	49	38.9 [a]	13	41.9 [a]	10	52.6 [a]		
50 to 59 years	64	50.8 [a]	17	54.8 [a]	7	36.8 [a]		
60 years or over	13	10.3 [a]	1	3.2 [a]	2	10.5 [a]		
Marital status							6.04	.643
Single	9	7.1 [a]	4	12.9 [a]	1	5.3 [a]		
Married	84	66.7 [a]	18	58.1 [a]	14	73.7 [a]		
Divorced	28	22.2 [a]	6	19.4 [a]	3	15.8 [a]		
Separated	4	3.2 [a]	2	6.5 [a]	0	0 [a]		

Widowed	1	[a]	1	3.2 [a]	1	5.3 [a]		
Annual household income							12.54	.251
Less than $30,000 per year	20	15.9 [ab]	0	0 [b]	5	26.3 [a]		
$30,001 to $50,000 per year	27	21.4 [a]	7	22.6 [a]	6	31.6 [a]		
$50,001 to $75,000 per year	27	21.4 [a]	8	25.8 [a]	5	26.3 [a]		
$75,001 to $100,000 per year	25	19.8 [a]	7	22.6 [a]	2	10.5 [a]		
$100,000 to 125,000 per year	12	9.5 [a]	5	16.1 [a]	1	5.3 [a]		
$125,001 or more per year	15	11.9 [a]	4	12.9 [a]	0	0 [a]		
Education level (4 groups)							14.21	.027
Up to a high school diploma	27	21.4 [a]	5	16.1 [a]	4	21.1 [a]		
Some college	60	47.6 [a]	10	32.3 [a]	10	52.6 [a]		
Bachelor's degree	29	23 [a]	6	19.4 [a]	3	15.8 [a]		
Graduate degree	10	7.9 [a]	10	32.3 [b]	2	10.5 [ab]		
VA rated							11.44	.324
Yes	71	56.3 [a]	18	58.1 [a]	9	47.4 [a]		
After years of delay	12	9.5 [a]	3	9.7 [a]	3	15.8 [a]		
Rating Denied	8	6.3 [a]	2	6.5 [a]	4	21.1 [a]		
Refused to Rate	0	0 [a]	1	3.2 [a]	0	0 [a]		
Pending Completion	8	6.3 [a]	2	6.5 [a]	1	5.3 [a]		
Did Not Try	27	21.4 [a]	5	16.1 [a]	2	10.5 [a]		
VA doctors paid attention							7.48	.279
None	30	23.8 [a]	4	12.9 [a]	2	10.5 [a]		
Rarely	36	28.6 [a]	11	35.5 [a]	6	31.6 [a]		
Occasionally	40	31.7 [a]	9	29 [a]	10	52.6 [a]		
Often	20	15.9 [a]	7	22.6 [a]	1	5.3 [a]		
Physically or emotionally disabled by experience in the Gulf War							9.88	.130
I was physically disabled	10	7.9 [a]	5	16.1 [a]	2	10.5 [a]		
I was emotionally disabled	34	27 [a]	15	48.4 [a]	7	36.8 [a]		
I was both physically and emotionally disabled	51	40.5 [a]	7	22.6 [a]	5	26.3 [a]		

None of these apply	31	24.6 [a]	4	12.9 [a]	5	26.3 [a]		
Gulf War Syndrome diagnosis							1.90	.754
I have been formally diagnosed with GWS by my physician	19	15.1 [a]	6	19.4 [a]	1	5.3 [a]		
I have not been formally diagnosed with GWS, but I do have symptoms of GWS	89	70.6 [a]	21	67.7 [a]	15	78.9 [a]		
I have not been diagnosed and I don't have symptoms consistent with GWS	18	14.3 [a]	4	12.9 [a]	3	15.8 [a]		

Note. For each row category, pairs of column proportions with different superscripts differed significantly, $p < 0.05$.

Table 7 provides demographics for marital status. A greater proportion of males were married (88.8%) as compared to those who were single or widowed (64.7%) or as compared to those who were divorced or separated (62.8%). A smaller proportion of females were married (11.2%) as compared to those who were single or widowed (35.3%) or those who were divorced or separated (37.2%). A greater proportion of participants who earned less than $30,000 per year were divorced or separated (27.9%), as compared to those who were married (7.8%).

Table 7. *Frequencies and Percentages for Demographic Variables by Marital Status*

	Single or Widowed		Married		Divorced or Separated			
Variable	*n*	%	*n*	%	*n*	%	χ^2	*p*
Gender							16.12	.001
Male	11	64.7 [a]	103	88.8 [b]	27	62.8 [a]		
Female	6	35.3 [a]	13	11.2 [b]	16	37.2 [a]		
Race/ethnicity (3 groups)							12.84	.118

White/ Caucasian	10	58.8 [a]	84	72.4 [a]	32	74.4 [a]		
Black/African American	5	29.4 [a]	18	15.5 [a]	8	18.6 [a]		
Other race/ ethnicity	2	11.8 [a]	14	12.1 [a]	3	7.0 [a]		
Age							4.27	.371
40 to 49 years	8	47.1 [a]	47	40.5 [a]	17	39.5 [a]		
50 to 59 years	9	52.9 [a]	55	47.4 [a]	24	55.8 [a]		
60 years or over	0	.0 [a]	14	12.1 [a]	2	4.7 [a]		
Annual household income							4.27	.371
Less than $30,000 per year	4	23.5 [ab]	9	7.8 [b]	12	27.9 [a]		
$30,001 to $50,000 per year	5	29.4 [a]	21	18.1 [a]	14	32.6 [a]		
$50,001 to $75,000 per year	4	23.5 [a]	30	25.9 [a]	6	14.0 [a]		
$75,001 to $100,000 per year	4	23.5 [a]	22	19.0 [a]	8	18.6 [a]		
$100,000 to 125,000 per year	0	.0 [a]	16	13.8 [a]	2	4.7 [a]		
$125,001 or more per year	0	.0 [a]	18	15.5 [a]	1	2.3 [a]		
Education level (4 groups)							2.49	.870
Up to a high school diploma	4	23.5 [a]	22	19.0 [a]	10	23.3 [a]		
Some college	6	35.3 [a]	54	46.6 [a]	20	46.5 [a]		
Bachelor's degree	4	23.5 [a]	24	20.7 [a]	10	23.3 [a]		
Graduate degree	3	17.6 [a]	16	13.8 [a]	3	7.0 [a]		
VA rated							13.84	.180
Yes	5	29.4 [a]	69	59.5 [a]	24	55.8 [a]		
After years of delay	4	23.5 [a]	7	6.0 [b]	7	16.3 [ab]		
Rating Denied	2	11.8 [a]	9	7.8 [a]	3	7.0 [a]		
Refused to Rate	0	.0 [a]	1	.9 [a]	0	.0 [a]		
Pending Completion	0	.0 [a]	8	6.9 [a]	3	7.0 [a]		
Did Not Try	6	35.3 [a]	22	19.0 [a]	6	14.0 [a]		
VA doctors paid attention							2.87	.825
None	5	29.4 [a]	24	20.7 [a]	7	16.3 [a]		

Rarely	4	23.5 [a]	33	28.4 [a]	16	37.2 [a]		
Occasionally	5	29.4 [a]	39	33.6 [a]	15	34.9 [a]		
Often	3	17.6 [a]	20	17.2 [a]	5	11.6 [b]		
Physically or emotionally disabled by experience in the Gulf War							6.29	.391
I was physically disabled	1	5.9 [a]	14	12.1 [a]	2	4.7 [a]		
I was emotionally disabled	5	29.4 [a]	33	28.4 [a]	18	41.9 [a]		
I was both physically and emotionally disabled	7	41.2 [a]	39	33.6 [a]	17	39.5 [a]		
None of these apply	4	23.5 [a]	30	25.9 [a]	6	14.0 [a]		
Gulf War Syndrome diagnosis							5.94	.204
I have been formally diagnosed with GWS by my physician	5	29.4 [a]	15	12.9 [a]	6	14.0 [a]		
I have not been formally diagnosed with GWS, but I do have symptoms of GWS	8	47.1 [a]	87	75.0 [a]	30	69.8 [a]		
I have not been diagnosed and I don't have symptoms consistent with GWS	4	23.5 [a]	14	12.1 [a]	7	16.3 [a]		

Note. For each row category, pairs of column proportions with different superscripts differed significantly, $p < 0.05$.

Table 8 provides demographics for diagnosis and disability. A greater proportion of those participants who were emotionally disabled (36.8%) reported not being formally diagnosed with GWS despite having symptoms, as compared to those who had not been diagnosed and did not have symptoms (12.0%). A greater proportion of participants who were physically and emotionally disabled (37.6%) reported not being formally diagnosed with GWS despite having symptoms, as compared to those who had not been diagnosed and did not have symptoms (8.0%). A greater proportion of participants checked "none of these apply" in response to the list of physical or emotional disabilities, had not been diagnosed, and did not have symptoms (72.0%), as compared to those who have been formally diagnosed with GWS (0.0%), or those who have not been diagnosed with GWS but do have symptoms (17.6%).

Table 8. *Frequencies and Percentages for Disabled by Diagnosis*

	Formally diagnosed with GWS		Not diagnosed but has GWS symptoms		Not diagnosed nor has symptoms			
Variable	*n*	%	*n*	%	*n*	%	χ^2	*p*
Physically or emotionally disabled by experience in the Gulf War							49.09	.001
I was physically disabled	5	19.2 [a]	10	8.0 [a]	2	8.0 [a]		
I was emotionally disabled	7	26.9 [ab]	46	36.8 [b]	3	12.0 [a]		
I was both physically and emotionally disabled	14	53.8 [a]	47	37.6 [a]	2	8.0 [b]		
None of these apply	0	.0 [a]	22	17.6 [a]	18	72.0 [b]		

Note. For each row category, pairs of column proportions with different superscripts differed significantly, $p < 0.05$.

The means and standard deviations for agent exposure by diagnosis is shown in Table 9. The means of agent exposure for each group were not statistically different from one another, F (2, 175) = 2.10, p = 0.126. This suggests that GWS diagnosis groups aren't related to the agent exposure counts. However, it is interesting to note that the group of veterans who did not have symptoms were exposed to fewer mean agents than those who identified themselves as having symptoms.

Table 9. *Mean and Standard Deviations for Agent Exposure by Diagnosis s*

Agent exposure count	*n*	*M*	*SD*	*F*	*p*	η^2_p
GWS diagnosis				2.10	.126	.024
I have been formally diagnosed with GWS by my physician	26	5.31 [a]	2.68			
I have not been formally diagnosed with GWS, but I do have symptoms of GWS	125	5.49 [a]	2.73			
I have not been diagnosed and I don't have symptoms consistent with GWS	25	4.28 [a]	2.49			

Note. Means with different superscripts differ significantly, $p < 0.05$.

There was a marginally significant relationship between agent exposure count and emotionally disabled participants. Participants who were both physically and emotionally disabled had higher agent exposure mean counts (6.30) as compared to participants who selected "none of these apply" in response to the list of disabilities (4.10).

Table 10. *Means and Standard Deviations for Agent Exposure by Disabled*

Agent exposure count	*n*	*M*	*SD*	*F*	*p*	η^2_p
Disability status				6.17	.001	.097
I was physically disabled	17	5.06 [ab]	2.63			
I was emotionally disabled	56	5.07 [ab]	2.71			
I was both physically and emotionally disabled	63	6.30 [b]	2.87			
None of these apply	40	4.10 [a]	1.85			

Note. Means with different superscripts differ significantly, $p < 0.05$.

A Pearson's product-moment correlational analysis was conducted to assess the bivariate relationships between the continuous study variables. The results are shown in Table 11. Agent exposure had a clear negative relationship with the RAND 36 survey subscales, with its strongest association being role limitations due to physical health (r = -0.291), $p <$ 0.001. Physical functioning had strong positive associations with all of the other health subscales, with the strongest being role limitations due to physical heath (r = 0.672), $p <$ 0.001. Social functioning had a strong positive relationship with emotional well-being (r = 0.651), $p <$ 0.001. Role limitations, due to emotional problems, had a strong positive relationship with emotional well-being (r = 0.619), $p <$ 0.001.

Table 11. *Pearson's Product–Moment Correlations Among Study Variables*

Variable		(1)	(2)	(3)	(5)
(1)	Agent exposure count	-			
(2)	Physical functioning mean	-0.201 **	-		
(3)	Social functioning mean	-0.172 *	.588 ***	-	
(4)	Emotional well-being mean	-0.092	.403 ***	.651 ***	
(5)	Role limitations due to physical health	-0.291 ***	.672 ***	.550 ***	-
(6)	Role limitations due to emotional problems	-0.197 **	.439 ***	.589 ***	.562 ***

Note. *$p <$ 0.05. **$p <$0.01. ***$p <$0.001.

Primary Analysis Results

RQ 1 asked: To what extent is chemical agent exposure related to physical functioning for veterans who suffered from GWS when controlling for demographic factors? The null hypothesis for this RQ stated that there was no association between chemical agent exposure and levels of physical functioning for GWS veterans when controlling for demographic factors. A multiple linear regression analysis was conducted to test this hypothesis and to answer the first research question. Table 11 shows the results of the analysis. Three models were run to test the effect of agent exposure, GWS diagnosis, and disability, respectively, while controlling for demographic characteristics. Each of these variables was added to the model to assess their individual contribution to the model and to control for confounding factors.

In Table 12, Model 1 consisted of physical functioning regressed on the demographic variables and the agent exposure count variable. The overall model was significant, F (16, 175) = 4.95, $p < 0.001$, $R^2 = 0.332$, adjusted $R^2 =$ 0.265, with the model explaining 26.5% of the variance in physical functioning. The results of the model indicated that males have lower physical functioning ($\beta = -10.46$, *Std.* $\beta = -0.0148$) as compared to females, $p < 0.05$. In terms of age, both the 50 to 59-year old group ($\beta = -9.44$, *Std.* $\beta = -0.167$) and the 60, or more, year-old ($\beta = -15.83$, *Std.* $\beta = -0.161$) age categories had lower physical functioning as compared to the youngest age group, *ps* < 0.05. A participant with a bachelor's degree ($\beta = 12.10$, *Std.* $\beta = 0.559$) had higher physical functioning compared to a participant with a high school degree, $p < 0.05$. Conversely, a participant with a graduate degree ($\beta =$ -44.49, *Std.* $\beta = -0.521$) had lower physical functioning as compared to a participant with a high school degree, $p < 0.05$. All of the income level categories had higher physical functioning when compared to the lowest income category, all *ps* < 0.05. The agent exposure count variable negatively predicted physical functioning ($\beta = -2.46$, *Std.* $\beta = -0.235$), $p = 0.001$. This suggested that as the number of agent exposure counts increased, levels of physical functioning decreased. There was no relationship between ethnicity/race and marital status on physical functioning.

Model 2 consisted of physical functioning regressed on the demographic variables, the agent exposure count variable with the GWS diagnosis variable added, and the non-symptomatic group as the reference category. The addition of the GWS diagnosis was meant to test the strength of the agent exposure variable. The overall model was significant, F (18, 175) = 5.88, $p < 0.001$, $R^2 = 0.402$, adjusted $R^2 = 0.334$, with the model explaining 33.4% of the variance in physical functioning. In this model, the 50-59 age group ($\beta = -8.26$, *Std.* $\beta = -0.146$) had lower physical functioning as compared to the youngest age group, ($p < 0.05$). All of the income level categories remained significant and had higher physical functioning when compared to the lowest income category, all *ps* < 0.05. The agent exposure count variable remained significant and negatively predicted physical functioning ($\beta = -1.91$, *Std.* $\beta = -0.182$), $p = 0.007$. The GWS diagnosis variable was significant in both participants who were diagnosed ($\beta = -19.70$, *Std.* $\beta = -0.317$) and were not diagnosed, but had symptoms ($\beta = -29.26$, *Std.* $\beta = -0.368$) and had lower physical as functioning compared to participants who were not diagnosed nor had symptoms. There was no relationship between gender, race/ethnicity, marital status, and education with physical functioning in this model.

Model 3 consisted of physical functioning regressed on the demographic variables, the agent exposure count variable, GWS diagnosis with the disability variable added, and the non-disability group as the reference category. The overall model was significant, F (21, 175) = 5.96, $p < 0.001$, $R^2 = 0.448$, adjusted $R^2 = 0.373$, with the model explaining 33.7% of the variance in physical functioning. In this model the 50-59 age group ($\beta = -8.23$, *Std.* $\beta = -0.146$) had lower physical functioning when compared to the youngest age group, $p < 0.05$. All of the income level categories remained significant and had higher physical functioning when compared to the lowest income category, all *ps* < 0.05. The agent exposure count variable remained significant and negatively predicted physical functioning ($\beta = -1.45$, *Std.* $\beta = -0.139$), $p = 0.043$. The GWS diagnosis variable was significant and both participants who were diagnosed ($\beta = -15.77$, *Std.* $\beta = -0.253$) and were not diagnosed, but had symptoms, ($\beta = -21.03$, *Std.* $\beta = -0.264$) had lower physical functioning when compared to participants who were not diagnosed, nor had symptoms. Those participants who identified as being both physically and emotionally disabled ($\beta = -12.53$, *Std.* $\beta = -0.213$) had lower physical functioning when compared to participants who indicated that they had no physical or emotional disability, $p < 0.05$. There was no relationship between gender, race/ethnicity, marital status, and education with physical functioning in this model.

In sum, the results of this analysis indicated that agent exposure had a statistically significant negative relationship to physical functioning, controlling for demographics, GWS diagnosis and disability. Therefore,

HI_0 was rejected and the alternative hypothesis was accepted. In addition, the GWS diagnosis variable also had a significant impact on explaining physical functioning in GWVs, with a 6.9% increase in explained variations of physical functioning over the agent exposure model.

Table 12. *Summary of Multiple Regression Analysis of Agent Exposure, Diagnosis, and Disabled Predicting Physical Functioning*

	Physical Functioning								
	Model 1			Model 2			Model 3		
Predictors	β	*Std. β*	*p*	β	*Std. β*	*p*	β	*Std. β*	*p*
Constant	53.88		.001	71.65		.001	71.25		.001
Male[a]	-10.46	-0.148	.045	-9.62	-0.136	.053	-8.26	-0.117	.092
Age (50 to 59)[b]	-9.44	-0.167	.018	-8.26	-0.146	.031	-8.23	-0.146	.027
Age (60 or older)[b]	-15.83	-0.161	.025	-12.90	-0.131	.056	-11.37	-0.116	.085
Ethnicity White[c]	-7.49	-0.120	.232	-5.13	-0.082	.393	-5.10	-0.082	.384
Ethnicity Black[c]	-13.92	-0.188	.066	-10.15	-0.137	.162	-9.56	-0.129	.177
Marital status (divorced)[d]	6.34	.097	.205	4.44	.068	.353	4.43	.067	.344
Marital status (single)[d]	1.12	.012	.870	-0.50	-0.005	.939	-0.10	-0.001	.987
Education (some college)[e]	6.30	.111	.215	4.17	.074	.392	5.70	.101	.241
Education (bachelor's degree)[e]	12.10	.559	.046	7.63	.353	.192	10.71	.495	.066
Education (graduate)[e]	-44.49	-0.521	.042	-24.92	-0.292	.241	-35.90	-0.421	.088
Income ($30,001 to $50,000 per year)[f]	23.20	.344	.001	20.01	.297	.001	17.25	.256	.005
Income ($50,000 to $75,000 per year)[f]	22.62	.336	.001	20.35	.302	.002	18.82	.279	.003
Income ($75,001 to $100,000 per year)[f]	34.34	.480	.001	28.78	.403	.001	27.26	.381	.001

Income ($100,001 to $125,000 per year)[f]	41.91	.450	.001	35.17	.378	.001	37.02	.398	.001
Income ($125,001 or more per year)[f]	47.37	.521	.001	38.93	.428	.001	34.98	.385	.001
Agent exposure count	-2.46	-0.235	.001	-1.91	-0.182	.007	-1.45	-0.139	.043
GWS not diagnosed but has symptoms[g]				-19.70	-0.317	.001	-15.77	-0.253	.008
GWS diagnosed and has symptoms[g]				-29.26	-0.368	.001	-21.03	-0.264	.006
Disabled (physical)[h]							-21.12	-0.221	.004
Disabled (emotional)[h]							-2.87	-0.047	.606
Disabled (both)[h]							-12.53	-0.213	.026

Note. Model 1: $F(16, 175) = 4.95, p < 0.001, R2 = .332$, adjusted $R2 = 0.265$. Model 2: $F(18, 175) = 5.88, p < 0.001, R2 = 0.402$, adjusted $R2 = 0.334$. Model 3: $F(21, 175) = 5.96, p < 0.001, R2 = 0.448$, adjusted $R2 = 0.373$. [a]Compared to Female. [b]Compared to 40 to 49 years of age. [c]Compared to "Other" race. [d]Compared to Married. [e]Compared to "up to a HS diploma." [f]Compared to Less than $30,000 per year. [g]Compared to "no diagnosis or symptoms". [h]Compared to "disability does not apply."

Table 13 provides demographics for physical functioning as a significant positive predictor of social functioning. As physical functioning increased, social functioning also increased. The ages category of 60+ was determined to be a significant positive predictor of social functioning as compared to the age groups below 50 years of age. Emotional disability was a significant, negative predictor of social functioning when compared to participants with no physical or emotional disability. Therefore, there was no association between levels of physical functioning and levels of social functioning for GWS veterans controlling for demographic factors.

Table 13. *Summary of Multiple Regression Analysis of Physical Functioning Predicting Social Functioning*

	Social Functioning		
Predictors	B	*Std. β*	*p*
Constant	29.23		.005
Male	.15	.002	.975
Age (50-59)	-0.74	-0.013	.840
Age (60+)	14.93	.144	.025
Ethnicity white	12.98	.200	.027
Ethnicity black	14.57	.192	.038
Marital status (divorced)	-3.70	-0.055	.416
Marital status (single)	5.85	.060	.342
Education (some college)	-2.32	-0.039	.616
Education (bachelor's degree)	-1.40	-0.063	.805
Education (graduate)	6.63	.076	.744
Income ($30,001 to $50,000 per year)	.61	.009	.921
Income ($50,000 to $75,000 per year)	.79	.011	.899
Income ($75,001 to $100,000 per year)	.15	.002	.983
Income ($100,001 to $125,000 per year)	-5.79	-0.061	.491
Income ($125,001 or more per year)	.64	.007	.938
Physical functioning mean	.47	.446	.001
Disabled (physical)	-28.36	-0.282	.001
Disabled (emotional)	-27.31	-0.435	.001
Disabled (both)	-28.26	-0.462	.001

Note. Model 1: $F(19, 169) = 8.43$, $p < 0.001$, $R^2 = 0.516$, adjusted $R^2 = 0.455$. [a]Compared to Female. [b]Compared to 40 to 49 years of age. [c]Compared to "Other" race. [d]Compared to Married. [e]Compared to "up to a HS diploma." [f]Compared to Less than $30,000 per year. [g]Compared to "no diagnosis or symptoms". [h]Compared to "disability does not apply"

Table 14 provides a demographic of physical functioning as related to emotional functioning. Emotional disability was a significant, negative predictor of emotional functioning, when compared to participants with no physical or emotional disability. Physical and emotional disability was a significant, negative predictor of emotional functioning when compared to participants with no physical or emotional disability. Income ($75,001-$100,000 per year) was a significant, positive predictor of emotional functioning when compared to the under $30,000 income group. There was no association between levels of physical functioning and levels of emotional well-being for GWS veterans when controlling for demographic factors.

Table 14. *Summary of Multiple Regression Analysis of Physical Functioning Predicting Emotional Functioning*

	Emotional Well-Being		
Predictors	β	*Std. β*	*p*
Constant	47.48		.001
Male	-4.04	-0.074	.321
Age (50-59)	1.16	.026	.711
Age (60+)	13.45	.172	.017
Ethnicity white	-1.40	-0.028	.776
Ethnicity black	1.47	.026	.804
Marital status (divorced)	-0.02	.000	.996
Marital status (single)	.80	.011	.878
Education (some college)	.65	.015	.870
Education (bachelor's degree)	-4.38	-0.261	.366
Education (graduate)	15.69	.237	.365
Income ($30,001 to $50,000 per year)	6.05	.114	.246
Income ($50,000 to $75,000 per year)	8.60	.161	.106
Income ($75,001 to $100,000 per year)	13.50	.240	.019
Income ($100,001 to $125,000 per year)	6.65	.090	.358
Income ($125,001 or more per year)	16.72	.232	.019
Physical functioning mean	.16	.202	.015
Disabled (physical)	-9.46	-0.124	.126
Disabled (emotional)	-23.50	-0.492	.001
Disabled (both)	-23.31	-0.503	.001

Note. Model 1: $F(19, 167) = 5.25$, $p < 0.001$, $R^2 = 0.403$, adjusted $R^2 = 0.326$. [a]Compared to Female. [b]Compared to 40 to 49 years of age. [c]Compared to "Other" race. [d]Compared to Married. [e]Compared to "up to a HS diploma." [f]Compared to Less than $30,000 per year. [g]Compared to "no diagnosis or symptoms". [h]Compared to "disability does not apply."

Model 1

Role Limitations Due to Physical Health

Physical functioning was a significant, positive predictor of physical health role limitations; as physical functioning scores increase so do physical health role limitations. Physical disability was a significant, negative predictor of physical health role limitations when compared to participants with no physical or emotional disabilities. Emotional disability was a significant negative predictor of physical health role limitations when compared to participants with no physical or emotional disabilities. Physical and emotional disability were significant, negative predictors of physical health role limitations when compared to participants with no physical or emotional disabilities.

Model 2

Role Limitations Due to Emotional Health

Physical functioning was a significant, positive predictor of emotional health role limitations. As physical functioning scores increased so did emotional health role limitations. Physical disability was a significant, negative predictor of emotional health role limitations when compared to participants with no physical or emotional disabilities. Emotional disability was a significant, negative predictor of emotional health role limitations when compared to participants with no physical or emotional disabilities. There is no association between levels of physical functioning and levels of role limitations for GWS veterans when controlling for demographic factors. Table 15 provides the demographics of physical functioning predicting physical and emotional role limitations.

Table 15. *Summary of Multiple Regression Analysis of Physical Functioning Predicting Physical and Emotional Role Limitations*

	Model 1: Limitations due to physical Health			Model 2: Limitations due to emotional health		
Predictors	β	*Std. β*	*p*	β	*Std. β*	*p*
Constant	12.29		.335	56.83		.001
Male	-6.47	-0.067	.279	.47	.005	.945
Age (50-59)	1.58	.020	.728	-7.38	-0.091	.159
Age (60+)	3.58	.026	.663	2.67	.019	.776
Ethnicity white	-2.90	-0.034	.688	-0.14	-0.002	.986
Ethnicity black	15.03	.148	.084	-0.09	-0.001	.993
Marital status (divorced)	.17	.002	.977	-9.46	-0.101	.146
Marital status (single)	.89	.007	.908	-3.33	-0.025	.703
Education (some college)	-1.44	-0.018	.802	10.20	.125	.122
Education (bachelor's degree)	12.73	.429	.072	10.41	.340	.198
Education (graduate)	-47.35	-0.406	.062	-40.19	-0.333	.166
Income ($30,001 to $50,000 per year)	-1.62	-0.017	.831	-2.90	-0.030	.739
Income ($50,000 to $75,000 per year)	-4.71	-0.050	.545	-4.70	-0.048	.598

Income ($75,001 to $100,000 per year)	2.05	.021	.806	-14.26	-0.139	.139
Income ($100,001 to $125,000 per year)	-12.51	-0.098	.232	2.29	.017	.848
Income ($125,001 or more per year)	5.09	.040	.623	1.17	.009	.921
Physical functioning mean	.72	.510	.001	.32	.220	.004
Disabled (physical)	-27.36	-0.204	.003	-43.58	-0.314	.001
Disabled (emotional)	-18.73	-0.224	.004	-48.87	-0.564	.001
Disabled (both)	-27.43	-0.336	.001	-54.78	-0.648	.001

Note. Model 1: $F(19, 169) = 10.93, p < 0.001, R^2 = 0.581$, adjusted $R^2 = 0.528$. Model 2: $F(19, 169) = 7.43, p < 0.001, R^2 = 0.485$, adjusted $R^2 = 0.420$. [a]Compared to Female. [b]Compared to 40 to 49 years of age. [c]Compared to "Other" race. [d]Compared to Married. [e]Compared to "up to a HS diploma." [f]Compared to Less than $30,000 per year. [g]Compared to "no diagnosis or symptoms". [h]Compared to "disability does not apply."

Implications of the Findings

This quantitative, correlational non-experimental study has significant implications for GWVs. The literature showed that GWVs have been affected by different health illnesses and their well-being from service in the Gulf War. In addition, it has been investigated that the GWS influences GWVs' well-being, as well as veterans who served in the Persian Gulf War. The framework of the study focused on four premises that influenced GWV well-being, physical functioning, social functioning, and role functioning, as well as agent exposure.

Results for Hypotheses 1

There was a significant negative association between agent exposure count and physical functioning mean. Therefore, $H1_0$ was rejected and the alternative hypothesis was accepted. In addition, the GWS diagnosis variable also has a significant mutual relationship with physical functioning in GWVs with a 6.9% increase in explained variation of physical functioning, over the agent exposure model.

Results for Hypotheses 2

There was a positive significant association between levels of physical functioning and levels of social functioning for GWS veterans, controlling for demographic factors. Physical functioning is a significant positive predictor of social functioning. As physical functioning increased, social functioning increased.

Results for Hypothesis 3

There was a significant association between levels of physical functioning and levels of emotional well-being for GWS veterans, controlling for demographic factors. Those participants who identified as being both physically and emotionally disabled ($\beta = -12.53$, *Std.* $\beta = -0.213$) had lower physical functioning compared to participants who indicated that they had no physical or emotional disability, $p < 0.05$. There was no relationship between gender, race/ethnicity marital status, and education with physical functioning in this model. The results of the *t*-tests confirmed the statistically significant correlation and therefore the null hypothesis was rejected.

Results for Hypotheses 4

Physical functioning was a significant positive predictor of emotional health role limitations – as physical functioning scores increased, so did emotional health role limitations. Therefore, $H1_0$ was rejected and the alternative hypothesis was accepted. Physical disability was a significant negative predictor of emotional health role limitations, compared to participants with no physical or emotional disability. Emotional disability was a significant negative predictor of emotional health role limitations, compared to participants with no physical or emotional disability. There was no association between levels of physical functioning and levels of role limitations for GWV's controlling for demographic factors.

Summary

The purpose of this quantitative, correlation study was to determine whether and to what extent there was a correlation between agent exposures and disabilities within the physical functioning of this veteran population. This study explored the link between exposures, disabilities, physical function, and other measures of veteran well-being such as; social, emotional, and role functioning. The formulation of the research questions served to investigate whether there was a correlation between veterans who served in the Gulf War and veterans' well-being. The RAND 36-item health survey was used to collect data on the study participants. There was a marginally significant relationship between agent exposure count and emotionally disabled participants. Participants who were both physically and emotionally disabled had a higher agent exposure mean count (6.30), as compared to participants who indicated none of these applied regarding their disability (4.10). There was a significant, positive association between physical, social and emotional functioning, as well as role limitation, due to physical problems. However, there was a significant, negative association between physical functioning. GWVs continue to report poorer heath than other war veterans even 20 years after the Gulf War (Porter, Long, & Rull, 2018). Chronic disease management and interventions to improve health and well-being among both Gulf War and Afghan Era veterans are essential. GWVs reported a higher occurrence of almost all measured physical functioning and mental health conditions (Porter, Long, & Rull, 2018). The GWV population, however, has a significant burden of disease including high role limitations and multiple chronic medical conditions (Porter, Long, & Rull, 2018). Goals and objections of the study, limitation, significance of the study, significance of study to leadership, recommendation for future research and conclusion are discussed in Chapter 5.

CHAPTER 5

Conclusion and Recommendations

Goals and Objectives of the Study

The purpose of this quantitative, correlational study was to examine the physical, social and emotional functioning, as well as well-being experienced by veterans who served in the Gulf War. Additionally, the research study tested whether chemical agent exposure or disability status was related to physical functioning issues such as social and emotional functioning, well-being, and physical functioning, role limitations; as measured by the RAND 36-item health survey. The findings revealed the impact of exposures on service members who served in the Gulf War and gave insight concerning their long-term well-being. Accordingly, these findings can have a potential effect on veterans' health policies and disability compensation. Findings from this study are also applicable for developing new initiatives for service-connected disability claims by VA management and for military leaders to use for fairly assessing the long-term impacts of GWS.

Limitations

It is important to acknowledge limitations that were integral to the investigation. First, the focus of the study was on the GWVs that served between 1990 and 1992 in the Persian Gulf. The scope of this study was limited to GWVs on Facebook with the authorization of the administrator of that group. Conclusions cannot be generalized to other GWVs during another time. Another limitation was timeframe.

During the first month of data collection, GWVs were resistant to taking the survey as they believed the study would not result in helping GWVs and as a result of their mistrust regarding providing information about themselves. Over time, GWVs became more accustomed to and increasingly comfortable with the process. In addition, the researcher did not consider the potential influence of other factors that may be related to GWV resistance, such as fear of taking a survey, biased opinions, or the possible influence of other GWVs.

Significance of the Study

According to DoD reports, one in four of the 697,000 service members who deployed during the Gulf War suffers from undiagnosed illnesses. These diseases are attributed to toxins, medication distributed by the military, and pesticides (Wilborn, 2009). Service members may also be affected by a cocktail of mixtures consisting of depleted uranium, pesticides, low-level sarin, PB, and multiple vaccines such as yellow fever, typhoid, hepatitis B and anthrax. The current investigation, and subsequent research, may answer questions of GWS concerning service members who deployed to the Gulf War. Although service members left the United States in good health, some returned from the Gulf War with undiagnosed illnesses (Foldvary, 2008). Given the results of the current study, military leaders may be able to modify leadership development and staff education programs to assist in helping government officials to understand, and work to solve stereotyping from some adversaries, that GWS is not an unknown illness. The outcomes from the research may provide evidence to the researcher and veterans who participated in the Gulf War.

Significance of the Current Study to Leadership

Researching these illnesses may assist in determining the best practices and strategies for politicians and military leaders, allowing them to embrace the numerous challenges that need to be addressed. The controversial nature of the GWS, regarding symptoms and possible causes, needs congressional leadership to support every study finding in the area of GWS to provide answers to veterans who may have suffered an illness while serving in the Gulf War (Hilborne, 2009). According to Hall (2008), the government may have inadvertently exposed veterans to experimental vaccines such as anthrax with adjuvants to create a stronger immune response to vaccines without their consent. The unethical nature of such studies puts the role of congressional leadership into question, and the Department of Veteran Affairs to make these finding public to veterans.

Implications of the Study

Research studies by the National Academies conducted over the last decade provide compelling evidence that Gulf War (GWS) may have been caused by exposure to chemicals, such as PB and various pesticides (Foldvary, 2008). These studies also show that physical functioning, role functioning, and social functioning that are involved in processing veteran well-being, as well as intellect pathways involved in controlling pain and fatigue, are altered in GWVs with GWS. Even now, 25 years after its conclusion, GWVs with GWS continue to experience complex health symptoms, and GWS remains challenging to analyze since the current GWS research process is limited by having to use information that has been self-reported in regard to symptoms.

Recommendations for Future Research

This quantitative, correlational study explored veterans' well-being that served in the Gulf War. While time has elapsed since most veterans have served in the military the VA maintain there is no definitive scientific studies that link symptoms and diseases. Additional research, including Gulf War 2 veterans, and those who may have served during a later date such as 2001, may result in validating conclusions drawn here. In the current study, most participants were male, with incomes of between $50,000 and $60,000. Furthermore, research regarding GWVs that may have served during a different time may afford a correlational of GWV's social and physical roles, and well-being. Numerous issues are known or alleged to impact the well-being and health status of Gulf War Veteran that served in the Persian Gulf such as neurological issues, fatigue, sleep problems, memory lost and other medical problems (Voelker, 1999).

The implications of declining physical and social functioning as well as overall well-being was a clear indication for additional research. These variables physical functioning, role functioning, social functioning, and agent exposure were known to vary across veteran status and therefore determined to be included into this study. Future research should gauge whether socioeconomic status, or other confounding factors, are responsible for the association of symptoms with poor health in GWVs (Voelkner, 1999). The validity of health decline status of GWV, and the identified health symptoms, should be evaluated using available health services and other research studies.

Conclusion

Chapter 5 concludes the research study. Through this correlational study, the researcher analyzed the physical functioning, role functioning, social functioning, and well-being of GWVs who served in the Persian Gulf region from 1990-1992. The findings in the study revealed a greater proportion of participants, that were emotionally disabled, who reported not being formally diagnosed with GWS, despite having symptoms. However, a larger proportion of participants, who reported role functioning none of these applied to their physical or emotional disabilities. Participants that have not been diagnosed and did not have symptoms as compared to those who have been formally diagnosed with GWS or those who have not been diagnosed with GWS but do have symptoms. Data analysis was useful in investigating the hypotheses of the research study. The results of the study revealed a significant relationship between veterans who served in the Gulf War and their well-being, who had not been diagnosed with GWS and had minimal symptoms. The study confirmed that a greater proportion of respondents indicated that VA doctors paid attention to the veteran well-being were older than 60 years of age as compared to 40-49-year-old veterans. Other outcomes of the study revealed a significant relationship between physical functioning and emotional functioning. Emotional disability was a significant, negative predictor of emotional health role limitations when compared to participants with no physical or emotional disabilities. Consequently, if veterans were not suffering from emotional or physical disabilities, they believed that agent exposure is related to their well-being. There was a significant, positive association between role limitations due to physical health and physical functioning, role limitations due to emotional problems, and social functioning means. There was also a significant, negative association between physical functioning mean and agent exposure count. The demographics of the sample for the study contributed information that supported previous research that GWS has an impact on their well-being. The complications from GWS was explained by several authors who researched the opportunities by which to educate the health community and the VA on origins and possible treatments for service members who severed in the Persian Gulf War (Chartrand & Siegel, 2007; Carpenter, 2014; Caress, 2001). In summary, the current data from the Gulf War Survey does support the existence of GWS as a factor in physical functioning, social functioning, and role functioning. Data also supports the contention that chemical agents have impacted veterans' well-being. The data did not support a hypothesized model without GWS, instead accounting for the symptoms according to the individual veteran participants. In the opinion of this researcher, future considerations should focus on treatment options for GWS, perhaps examining the handling of veteran well-being. Regardless of whether GWS are comprised of distinct, medically unexplainable illnesses, GWVs deserve enhance on-going studies and research into the causes of GWS and their well-being. The contribution of this research may support that there is a need for additional educations to provide insight into GWS.

References

Abouzeid, M., Kelsall, H. L., Forbes, A. B., Sim, M. R., & Creamer, M. C. (2012). Posttraumatic stress disorder and hypertension in Australian veterans of the 1991 Gulf War. *Journal of Psychosomatic Research, 72*(1), 33-38. doi:10.1016/j.jpsychores.2011.08.002

Al-Khodairy, F., Al-Dakan, A., Akel, M., & Hannan, M. A. (1998). A comparative analysis of mutagenic activities of air samples collected from Riyadh before, during and after the Gulf War. *International Journal of Environmental Health Research, 8*(1), 15-22. doi:10.1080/09603129873615

Al-Turkait, F., & Ohaeri, J. U. (2008). Prevalence and correlates of posttraumatic stress disorder among Kuwaiti military men according to level of involvement in the first Gulf War. *Depression and Anxiety, 25*(11), 932-941. doi:10.1002/da.20373

Batten, S. V., & Pollack, S. J. (2008). Integrative outpatient treatment for returning service members. *Journal of Clinical Psychology, 64*(8), 928-939. doi:10.1002/jclp.20513

Bilmes, L. (2007). *The cost of the war: A comment on Stiglitz-Bilmes*. Retrieved from https://www.cbo.gov/publication/24762

Burns, N., & Grove, S. K. (2005). *The practice of nursing research: Conduct, critique, and utilization* (5th ed.). St. Louis, MO: Elsevier Saunders.

Caress, S. M. (2001). Organizational impediments to effective policy of Gulf War Syndrome. *Policy Studies Journal, 29*(2), 250-262. doi:10.1111/j.1541-0072.2001.tb02089.x

Carpenter, D. (2014). *Gulf War Syndrome: Evaluation of an innovation of detoxification program*. Retrieved from: http://www.dtic.mil/dtic/tr/fulltext/u2/1007348.pdf

Chartrand, M. M., & Siegel, B. (2007). At war in Iraq and Afghanistan: Children in US military families. *Ambulatory Pediatrics, 7*(1), 1-2. doi:10.1016/j.ambp.2006.11.004

Chaumba, J. & Bride, B. E. (2010). Trauma experiences and posttraumatic stress disorder among women in the United States military. *Social Work and Mental Health, 8*(3), 280-303. doi:10.1080/15332980903328557

Cherry, N., Creed, F., Silman, A., Dunn, G., Baxter, G., Smedley, J., Macfarlane, G. J. (2001). Health and exposures of United Kingdom Gulf War veterans. Part II: The relation of health to exposure. *Journal of Occupational and Environmental Medicine, 58*(5), 299-306. doi:10.1136/oem.58.5.299

Chong, J.-R. (2008, March 11). Gulf War syndrome theory upheld. *Los Angeles Times.* Retrieved from http://articles.latimes.com/2008/mar/11/science/sci-gulf11

Chor, D. (2010). Unpacking sources of comparative advantage: A quantitative approach. *Journal of International Economics, 82*(2), 152–167. doi:10.1016/j.jinteco.2010.07.004

Cooper, D. R., & Schindler, P. S. (2011). *Business research methods* (11th ed.). Boston, MA: McGraw-Hill Irwin.

Coscarelli, W., & Shrock, S. (2002). The two most useful approaches to estimating criterion-referenced test reliability in a single test administration. *Performance Improvement Quarterly, 15*(14), 74-85. doi:10.1111/j.1937-8327.2002.tb00266.x

Creswell, J. W. (2007). *Educational research: Planning, conducting, and evaluating quantitative and qualitative research* (3rd Ed.). Upper Saddle River, NJ: Prentice Hall.

Creswell, J. W. (2009). *Research design: Qualitative, quantitative, and mixed method approaches* (3rd ed.). Los Angeles, CA: Sage.

Deahl, M. (2005). Smoke, mirrors, and Gulf War Syndrome. *The Lancet, 365*(9460), 635-638. doi:10.1016/s0140-6736(05)17960-4

Department of Veterans Affairs. (2007). Gulf War Veterans' Illnesses Task Force. Retrieved from https://www.va.gov/RAC-GWVI/docs/Gulf_War_Illnesses_Link

eEngdahl, R. M., Elhai, J. D., Richardson, J. D., & Frueh, B. C. (2011). Comparing posttraumatic stress disorder's symptom structure between deployed and nondeployed veterans. *Psychological Assessment, 23*(1), 1-6. doi:10.1037/a0020045

Engelhard, I. M., Arntz, A., & Hout, M. A. (2007). Low specificity of symptoms on the post-traumatic stress disorder (PTSD) symptom scale: A comparison of individuals with PTSD, individuals with other anxiety disorders and individuals without psychopathology. *British Journal of Clinical Psychology, 46*(4), 449–456. doi:10.1348/014466507x206883

Epidemiol. J (2011 Oct 1); Chronic HYPERLINK "https://www.ncbi.nlm.nih.gov/pubmed/25466246"multisymptomatic HYPERLINK "https://www.ncbi.nlm.nih.gov/pubmed/25466246" illness: a comparison of Iraq and Afghanistan deployers with veterans of the 1991 Gulf War.174(7):761-8. doi: 10.1093/

Field, A. (2013). *Discovering statistics using SPSS*, (4th Ed). Thousand Oaks, CA: Sage Publications Ltd.

Field, A. (2009). *Discovering statistics using SPSS*, (3rd Ed). Los Angeles, CA: Sage Publications Ltd.

Foldvary, F. E. (2008). Uncovering the costs of the Iraq War. *Econ Journal Watch, 5*(3), 373-379. Retrieved from https://www.researchgate.net/profile/Fred_Foldvary/publication/46530735_Uncovering_the_Costs_of_the_Iraq_War/links/0912f50b37bcd95007000000.pdf

Ford-Martin, P. A. (2005). Gulf War Syndrome. In J. L. Longe (Ed.), *The Gale encyclopedia of alternative medicine* , 2nd ed. (pp. 1495–1497). Detroit, MI: Gale Group.
Frost, J. (2000, February/Winter). Gulf War syndrome: Proposed causes. *Cleveland Clinic Journal of Medicine, (67)*(1), 17-20. Retrieved from https://www.mdedge.com/ccjm/article/93388/infectious-diseases/gulf-war-syndrome-proposed-causes
George, D., & Mallery, P. (2013). *IBM SPSS statistics 21 step by step: A simple guide and reference* (13th Ed.). Upper Saddle River, NJ: Pearson.
Golier, J. A., Schmeidler, J., & Yehuda, R. (2009). Pituitary response to metyrapone in Gulf War veterans: Relationship to deployment, PTSD and unexplained health symptoms. *Psychoneuroendocrinology, 34*(9), 1338-1345. doi:10.1016/j.psyneuen.2009.04.004
Gupta, M. A. (2013). Review of somatic symptoms in post-traumatic stress disorder. *International Review of Psychiatry, 25*(1), 86–99. doi:10.3109/09540261.2012.736367
Haley, R. W., Maddrey, A. M., & Gershenfeld, H. K. (2002). Severely reduced functional status in veterans fitting: A case definition of Gulf War Syndrome. *American Journal of Public Health, 92*(1), 46-47. doi:10.2105/ajph.92.1.46
Haley, R. W., Marshall, W. W., McDonald, G. G., Daugherty, M. A., Petty, F., & Fleckenstein, J. L. (2000). Brain abnormalities in Gulf War Syndrome: Evaluation with IH MR spectroscopy. *Radiology, 215*(3), 807-817. doi:10.1148/radiology.215.3.r00jn48807
Hall, H. (2008). Gulf War syndrome or Gulf lore mythology? *Skeptic, 14*(4), 26. Retrieved from http://connection.ebscohost.com/c/articles/37298906/
Hassija, C. M., Jakupack, M., Maguen, S., & Shipherd, J. C. (2012). The influence of combat and interpersonal trauma on PTSD, depression, and alcohol misuse in U.S. Gulf War and OEF/OIF women veterans. *Journal of Traumatic Stress, 25*(2), 216-219. doi:10.1002/jts.21686
Hilborne, L. H. (2009). Setting the stage for the second decade of the era of patient safety: contributions by the agency for healthcare research and quality and grantees. *Health Services Research, 44*(2 Pt 2), 623–627. doi:10.1111/j.1475-6773.2009.00949.x
Hisle-Gorman, E., Harrington, D., Nylund, C. M., Tercyak, K. P., Anthony, B. J., & Gorman, G. H. (2015). Impact of parents' wartime military deployment and injury on young children's safety and mental health. *Journal of the American Academy of Child and Adolescent Psychiatry, 54*(4), 294-301. doi:10.1016/j.jaac.2014.12.017
Hourani, L. L., Council, C. L., Hubal, R. C., & Strange, L. B. (2011). Approaches to the primary prevention of posttraumatic stress disorder in the military: A review of the stress control literature. *Military Medicine, 176*(7), 721-730. doi:10.7205/milmed-d-09-00227

Ikin, J. F., Sim, M. R., Creamer, M. C., Forbes, A. B., McKenzie, D. P., Kelsall, H. L., ... Schwarz, H. (2004). War-related psychological stressors and risk of psychological disorders in Australian veterans of the 1991 Gulf War. *British Journal of Psychiatry, 185*(2), 116–126. http://doi.org/10.1192/bjp.185.2.116

INFORMATION FOR VETERANS WHO SERVED IN DESERT SHIELD/STORM AND THEIR FAMILIES. (1999, August). *Gulf War Review Newsletter, 16*(1), 1-5. Retrieved from http://www.publichealth.va.gov/exposures/Gulf War

Institute of Medicine. 2008. *Gulf War and Health: Updated Literature Review of Depleted Uranium*. Washington, DC: The National Academies Press. https://doi.org/10.17226/12183.

Institute of Medicine. (1996). *Veterans and Agent Orange: Update 1996*. Washington, DC: National Academy Press.

Ismail, L. Petrik, M.S., Wong., M.C., Tabata, R. C. (2011). Gulf War Syndromees: Causes and controversies. *Pro Med* 20(6), 421-427.

Ismail, K., Kent, K., Sherwood, R., Hull, L., Seed, P., David, A. S., & Wessely, S. (2007). Chronic fatigue syndrome and related disorders in UK veterans of the Gulf War 1990-1991: Results from a two-phase cohort study. *Psychological Medicine, 38*(7), 953-961. doi:10.1017/s0033291707001560

Jakupcak, M., Conybeare, D., Phelps, L., Hunt, S., Holmes, H. A., Felker, B., ... & McFall, M. E. (2007). Anger, hostility, and aggression among Iraq and Afghanistan war veterans reporting PTSD and subthreshold PTSD. *Journal of Traumatic Stress,* 20(6), 945–954. doi:10.1002/jts.20258

Johnson, M. L., Rodriguez, H. P., & Solorio, M. R. (2010). Case-mix adjustment and the comparison of community health center performance on patient experience measures. *Health Service Research, 45*(3), 670–690. doi:10.1111/j.1475-6773.2010.01101.x

Jordan, B. K., Marmar, C. R., Fairbank, J. A., Schlenger, W. E., Kulka, R. A., Hough, R. L., & Weiss, D. S. (1992). Problems in families of male Vietnam veterans with posttraumatic stress disorder. *Journal of Consulting and Clinical Psychology, 60*(6), 916–926. doi:10.1037//0022-006x.60.6.916

Kang, H. K., Mahan, C. M., Lee, K. Y., Magee, C. A., & Murphy, F. M. (2000). Illnesses among United States veterans of the Gulf War: A population-based survey of 30,000 veterans. *Journal of Occupational and Environmental Medicine, 42*(5), 491-501. https://doi.org/10.1097/00043764-200005000-00006

Kennedy, K. (2007, May 26). Study: Sarin at root of Gulf War Syndrome. *Veterans Advantage*. Retrieved from https://www.veteransadvantage.com/va/vetnews/study-sarin-root-gulf-war-syndrome

Kerlinger, F. N. (1986). *Foundations of behavioral research*. New York, NY: Holt, Rinehart and Winston.

Khaylis, A., Polusny, M. A., Erbes, C. R., Gewirtz, A., & Rath, M. (2011). Posttraumatic stress, family adjustment, and treatment preferences among National Guard soldiers deployed to OEF/OIF. *Military Medicine, 176*(2), 126–131. doi:10.7205/milmed-d-10-00094

Kimerling R, Clum G. A., & Wolfe, J. (2000). Relationships among trauma exposure, chronic posttraumatic stress disorder symptoms, and self-reported health in women: Replication and extension. *Journal of Traumatic Stress, 13*(1), 115–128. doi:10.1023/a:1007729116133

Kime, P. (2015, January 27). Study links genetics, anti nerve-agent pills to Gulf War Syndrome. *Military Times.* Retrieved from https://www.militarytimes.com/veterans/2015/01/27/study-links-genetics-anti-nerve-agent-pills-to-gulf-war-illness/

Klare. M. T. (2006). Oil, Iraq, and American foreign policy: The continuing salience of the Carter Doctrine. *International Journal, 62*(1), 31–42. doi:10.2307/40204243

Kotlowski, C. A. (2009). *An exploratory study of military deployment and its impact on marriage and family of soldiers* (Doctoral dissertation). Retrieved from the University of Phoenix Dissertations and Theses database. (Publication No. AAT 3375978)

Lashof, J., & Cassell, J. (1998, September/Fall). Illness among Gulf War veterans: Risk factors, realities, and future research. *JAMA*, 280(11), 1010-1011. doi:10.1001/jama.280.11.1010

Levine, P. H. (2000, October 16). GWU studies symptoms of Gulf War vets. *GulfLINK.* Retrieved from http://www.gulflink.osd.mil/news/na_gwu_18oct00.html

Lidie, K. (2018). *Gulf War Illness Research Program Overview and Update.* Retrieved from https://www.va.gov/RAC-GWVI/meetings/mar2018/LidieMarch2018508

Litz, B. T., Keane, T. M., Fisher, L., Marx, B., & Monaco, V. (1992). Physical health complaints in combat-related post-traumatic stress disorder: A preliminary report. *Journal of Traumatic Stress,* 5(1), 131–141. doi:10.1007/bf00976818

Lobel, J., & Ratner, M. (2003). International law: The new Bush Doctrine and war with Iraq. *Guild Practitioner, 60*(4), 4-21. Retrieved from https://ssi.armywarcollege.edu/pubs/parameters/articles/03spring/record.pdf

Martin, G. J., & Tribble, D. R. (2010). The infectious diseases clinical research program: Addressing the challenge of infections related to war injuries and skin and soft tissues. *Military Medicine, 175*, 45-48. doi:10.7205/milmed-d-10-00157

McAllister, B. (Year1993, September 10). RIEGLE SUGGESTS IRAQ CONDUCTED CHEMICAL WARFARE. *Washington Post*, p.1

Mcfarlane, A. C., Atchinson, M., Rafalowicz, E., & Papay, P. (1994). Physical symptoms in post-traumatic stress disorder. *Journal of Psychosomatic Research, 38*(7), 715–726. doi:10.1016/0022-3999(94)90024-8

McHorney, C.A., Ware, J. E., & Raczek, A. E. (1993) The MOS 36-Item Short Form Health Survey (SF-36): II. Psychometric and clinical tests of validity in measuring physical and mental health constructs. *Medical Care. 31*(3): 247-253. doi:10.1097/00005650-199303000-00006

Mellman, T. A., Kulick-Bell, R., Ashlock, L. E., & Nolan, B. (1995). Sleep events among veterans with combat-related posttraumatic stress disorder. *American Journal of Psychiatry, 152*(1), 110-115. doi:10.1176/ajp.152.1.110

National Center for PTSD. (2007). *PTSD*. Retrieved from https://www.ptsd.va.gov/

Newman, I., & Covrig, D. M. (2013). Building consistency between title, problem statement, purpose, & research questions to improve the quality of research plans and reports. *New Horizons in Adult Education and Human Resource Development, 25*(1), 70-79. doi:10.1002/nha.20009

Nicolson, G. L., Bruton, D. M., & Nicolson, N. L. (1996). Chronic fatigue illness and Operation Desert Storm. *Journal of Occupational & Environmental Medicine, 38*(1), 14-16. doi:10.1097/00043764-199601000-00003

Null, G., & Flade, M. (2011, July). Gulf War syndrome: A deadly legacy. *Townsend Letter.* Retrieved from http://www.townsendletter.com/July2011/gulfwar0711.html

Olson, J. (Year2016, August 15). Still sick 25 years after the Gulf War, a vet seeks answers — and the Minneapolis VA may have them. *MINNEAPOLIS STAR-TRIBUNE*, p.1.

Orcutt, H. K., Erickson, D. J., & Wolfe, J. (2014). The course of PTSD symptoms among Gulf War veterans: A growth mixture modeling approach. *Journal of Traumatic Stress,17*(3), 195-202. doi:10.1023/B:JOTS.0000029262.42865.c2

O'Regan, R. (Producer). (2007, August 20). Gulf War Syndrome [Television series episode]. *Conspiracy Test.* Silver Spring, MD: Discovery Channel.

Pierce, P. F. (2005). Monitoring the health of Persian Gulf War veteran women. *Military Medicine, 170*(5), 349-354. doi:10.7205/MILMED.170.5.349

Pietrzak, R. H., Johnson, D. C., Goldstein, M. B., Malley, J. C., & Southwick, S. M. (2009). Perceived stigma and barriers to mental health care utilization among OEF-OIF veterans. *Psychiatric Services, 60*(8), 1118-1122. doi:10.1176/ps.2009.60.8.1118.

Popoola, E. O. (2011). *Intrinsic spirituality and posttraumatic stress disorder: A focus on the Canadian forces* (Doctoral dissertation). Retrieved from ProQuest Dissertations and Theses database.

Porter, B., Long, K., & Rull, R.P. (2018, May). Health Status of Gulf War and Era Veterans Serving in the US Military in 2000. *PubMed.gov, 60*(), 261-267. doi: doi: 10.1097/JOM.0000000000001280.

Radford, B. (2007). New report casts doubt on Gulf War syndrome. *The Skeptical Inquirer, 31*(1), 13–14. Retrieved from http://www.csicop.org/author/benradford/p60/P390

RAND Health Care. (2012). *36-item short form survey (SF-36)*. Retrieved from http://www.rand.org/health/surveys_tools/mos/36-item-short-form.html

Reed, S. C., Bell, J. F., & Edwards, T. C. (2011). Adolescent well-being in Washington state military families. *American Journal of Public Health, 101*(9), 1676-1682. doi:10.2105/ajph.2011.300165

Rempfer, T. (2009). The anthrax vaccine: A dilemma for Homeland Security. *Homeland Security Affairs, 5*(2), 1-12. Retrieved from https://www.hsaj.org/articles/102

Riddle, J. R., Brown, M., Smith, T., Richie, E. C., Brix, K. A., & Romano, J. (2003). Chemical warfare and the gulf war: A review of the impact on gulf veterans' health. *Military Medicine, 168*(8), 606-613. Retrieved from http://search.proquest.com/openview/5257736d66f0477ef754619c1dea0341/1?pq-origsite=gscholar

Salant, P., & Dillman, D. A. (1994). *How to conduct your own survey.* New York, NY: John Wiley and Sons.

Sartin, J. S. (2000). Gulf War Syndromees: Causes and controversies. *Mayo Clinic Proceedings, 75*(8), 811–819. doi:10.4065/75.8.811

Sayer, N. A., Friedemann-Sanchez, G., Spoont, M., Murdoch, M., Parker, L. E., Chiros, C., & Rosenheck, R. (2009). A qualitative study of determinants of PTSD treatment initiation in veterans. *Psychiatry: Interpersonal and Biological Processes, 72*(3), 238-255. doi:10.1521/psyc.2009.72.3.238.

Silverleib, A. (2012). Gulf War Syndrome is real, new federal report says. *CNN.* Retrieved from http://www.cnn.com/2008/HEALTH/11/17/gulf.war.illness.study/

Silvia, C. A. (2012). *Assessing body image from a parental and child's perspective* (Doctoral dissertation). Retrieved from ProQuest Dissertations and Theses database. (Accession No. 1334932866).

Simms, L. J., Watson, D., & Doebbelling, B. N. (2002). Confirmatory factor analyses of posttraumatic stress symptoms in deployed and nondeployed veterans of the Gulf War. *Journal of Abnormal Psychology, 111*(4), 637-647. doi:10.1037//0021-843X.111.4.637

Simon, M. K. (2011). *Dissertation and scholarly research: Recipes for success.* Retrieved from http://www.worldcat.org/title/dissertation-and-scholarly-research-recipes-for-success/oclc/762961545

Smith, M., & Liehr, P. (1999). *Nursing theory for the 21st century* (4th ed.). New York, NY: Springer.

Smyth, J. D., Dillman, D. A., Christian, L. M., & McBride, M. (2009). Open-ended questions in web surveys: Can increasing the size of answer boxes and providing extra verbal instructions improve response quality? *Public Opinion Quarterly, 73*(2), 325-337. doi:10.1093/poq/nfp029

Stecker, T., Fortney, J. C., Hamilton, F., & Ajzen, I. (2007). An assessment of beliefs about mental health care among veterans who served in Iraq. *Psychiatric Services,* 58(10), 1358-1361. doi:10.1176/ps.2007.58.10.1358

Steele, L. (2015). Prevalence and patterns of Gulf War Syndrome in Kansas veterans: Association of symptoms with characteristics of person, place, and time of military service. *American Journal of Epidemiology, 152*(10), 992-1002.

Steele, L., Sastre, A., Gerkovich, M. M., & Cook, M. R. (2012). Complex factors in the etiology of Gulf War Syndrome: Wartime exposures and risk factors in veteran subgroups. *Environmental Health Perspectives, 120*(1), 112–118. doi:10.1289/ehp.1003399

Stephey, M. J. (2008, November 20). The skimmer: Gulf War Syndrome. *Time.* Retrieved from http://content.time.com/time/health/article/0,8599,1860619,00.html

Stewart, A. L., Hays, R. D., & Ware, J. E. (1992). Health perceptions, energy/fatigue, and health distress measures. In A. L. Stewart & J. E. Ware; Jr. (Eds.), *Measuring functioning and well-being: The medical outcomes study approach* (pp. 143–172), Durham, NC: Duke University Press.

Stieger, S., & Reips, U. -D., (2010) What are participants doing while filling in an on-line questionnaire: A paradata collection tool and empirical study. *Human Behavior, 26*(6), 1488-1495. doi:10.1016/j.chb.2010.05.013

Stretch, R.H., Marlowe, D.H., & Wright, K.M. (1996, July). Post-Traumatic Stress Disorder Symptoms among Gulf War Veterans. *MILITARY MEDICINE, 161*(7), 407-409. Retrieved from https://watermark.silverchair.com/milmed-161-7-407.

Surís, A., & North, C. S. (2011). Diagnostic challenges of combat-related posttraumatic stress disorder. *Psychiatric Annals, 41*(8), 391-395. doi:10.3928/00485713-20110727-04

Sutker, P. B., Davis, J. M., Uddo, M., & Ditta, S. R. (2014). War zone stress, personal resources, and PTSD in Persian Gulf War returnees. *Journal of Abnormal Psychology, 104*(3), 444-452. doi:10.1037//0021-843X.104.3.444

Taft, C. T., Schumm, J. A., Panuzio, J., & Proctor, S. P. (2008). An examination of family adjustment among Operation Desert Storm veterans. *Journal of Consulting and Clinical Psychology, 76*(4), 648-656. doi:10.1037/a0012576

Trochim, W. M. K. (2006). *Time in research.* Retrieved from http://www.socialresearchmethods.net/kb/timedim.php

Tucker-Drob, E. M. (2011). Neurocognitive functions and everyday functions change together in old age. *Neuropsychology, 25*(3), 368–377. doi:10.1037/a0022348

U.S. Department of Defense. (2008). *Military family readiness policy and plans for the Department of Defense for the support of military family readiness.* Retrieved from http://www.militaryonesource.mil/footer?content_id=279106

U. S. Department of Veterans Affairs (2010). *Veterans' diseases associated with Agent Orange. Agent Orange.* Retrieved from http://www.publichealth.va.gov/exposures/agentorange/diseases.asp retrieved

Usher, A. (2008, November 16). Panel finds widespread Gulf War Syndrome. *Cox News Service.* Retrieved from http://vetshelpcenter.com/articles/gulf-war-syndrome/panel-finds-widespread-gulf-war-illness.html

Valdes, D. W. (2000). *Persian Gulf War Syndrome: The public policy syndrome* (Master's thesis). Retrieved from the University of Texas at El Paso's Digital Commons database. (Publication No. AAT EP05370).

Venkatraman, V., Huettel, S. A., Chuah, L. Y. M., Payne, J. W., & Chee, M. W. L. (2011). Sleep deprivation biases the neural mechanisms underlying economic preferences. *Journal of Neuroscience, 31(10),* 3712–3718. doi:10.1523/jneurosci.4407-10.2011

Vogt, D. (2011). Mental health-related beliefs as a barrier to service use for military personnel and veterans: A review. *Psychiatric Services,* 62(2), 135-142. doi:10.1176/ps.62.2.pss6202_0135.

Walker, C. A. (2003). Making assumptions explicit. *Journal of Theory Construction and Testing,* 7(2), 37. Retrieved from http://go.galegroup.com/ps/anonymous?id=GALE%7CA112129959

Ware, J. E., & Sherbourne, C. D. (1992). The MOS 36-item short-form health survey (SF-36): I. conceptual framework and item selection. *Medical Care, 30*(6), 473-483. doi:10.1097/00005650-199206000-00002

Weiner, M. W., Meyerhoff, D. J., Neylan, T. C., Hlavin, J., Ramage, E. R., McCoy, D., & McCarthy, C. (2011). The relationship between Gulf War Syndrome, brain n-acetylaspartate, and post-traumatic stress disorder. *Military Medicine, 176*(8), 896-902. Doi:10.7205/milmed-d-10-00332

Wilborn, T. (2009). *Study finds: Gulf War Syndrome is real.* Retrieved from https://www.thefreelibrary.com/Study+finds%3a+Gulf+War+illness+is+real.-a0192638453

Wilson, M. (2008). *Gulf War Syndrome.* Retrieved from http://www.merck.com

Wilson, F. R., Pan, W., & Schumsky, D. A. (2012). Recalculation of the critical values for Lawshe's content validity ratio. *Measurement and Evaluation in Counseling and Development, 45*(3), 197-210. doi:10.1177/0748175612440286

Wollack, J. A., Cohen, A. S. & Wells, C. S. (2003). A method for maintaining scale stability in the presence of test speededness. *Journal of Educational Measurement, 40*(4), 307-330. doi:10.1111/j.1745-3984.2003.tb01149.x

Wright, E. J. (2009). We are all responsible: Post-World War I parenting and the politics of war. *Literature and the Arts: An International Journal of the*

Humanities, 21(1/2), 277-298. Retrieved from http://connection.ebscohost.com/c/literary-criticism/48170396

Zapor, M.J., & Moran, K.A. (2005). Infectious diseases during wartime (3rd ed.). New York, NY: Mosby Publishing

Zoroya, G. (2012, March 22). Researchers wrestle with how many deployments are too many. *USA Today*. Retrieved from http://usatoday30.usatoday.com/news/military/story/2012-03-19/army-troops-deployments-bales/53691410/1

Zuckerman, D., & Olson, P. (1994, May). Is military research hazardous to veterans' health: *Preliminary Staff Findings extract*, ()

APPENDIX A

Research Study Advertisement and Flyer

GULF WAR SYNDROME'S EFFECTS ON THE WELL-BEING OF PERSIAN GULF VETERANS

Seeking veterans who served in the Gulf War and in the military during August, 1990 - December, 1992.

If you answered YES to the above question and you meet the requirement, you may be eligible to participate in a research study on Gulf War. The purpose of this study is to examine the different health symptoms and illnesses that Gulf War veterans exhibited upon returning from the Gulf War. The study aims to analyze the connection between the said health complications of the war-deployed veterans and the environmental and contextual factors that were existent in their area of deployment, as well as whether all post-war syndromes are related to Gulf War Syndromes. Participants will be required to complete survey. The survey will take approximately 30 minutes to complete. The study is being conducted at:

Local VSO, Internet use and email

APPENDIX B

Informed Consent Form

University of Phoenix®

Informed Consent: Participants 18 years of age and older

Dear ________________

My name is and I am a student at the University of Phoenix working on a Doctoral of Management degree. I am doing a research study entitled **GULF WAR SYNDROME'S EFFECTS ON THE WELL-BEING OF PERSIAN GULF VETERANS.** The purpose of the research study is to examine the different health symptoms and illnesses that the Gulf War veterans exhibited upon returning from the war. The aim of the study is to analyze the connection between the said health complications of the war-deployed veterans and the environmental and contextual factors that were existent in their area of deployment, as well as whether all post-war syndromes are related to Gulf War Syndromes. The study also looked at the backgrounds and health statuses of the war veterans before and after deployment to the Gulf War. Furthermore, the study also aims to understand the social impact of study findings on Gulf War Syndromes, particularly on political leaders and how they perceive and react to these findings. The purpose of this quantitative correlational study is to examine the health status of Gulf War veterans and those veterans who remained stateside and did not serve in the Gulf War to determine if both groups experience similar health complications as a result of their service. The study will analyze the connection between the health complications associated with post-Gulf war veterans and those of veterans who have served stateside to see if any major differences exist between both groups. Your participation will involve answering a short survey instrument that will ask your health symptoms and illnesses only. The survey will only take up to a maximum of 30 minutes. You would answer the survey questions electronically via e-mail. The researcher will send the survey questions through your e-mail once you will agree to participate in the study. You can decide to be a part of this study or not. Once you start, you can withdraw from the study at any time without any penalty or loss of benefits. The results of the research study may be published but your identity will remain confidential and your name will not be made known to any outside party.

In this research, there is no risk to you except "none".

Although there may be no direct benefit to you, a possible benefit from your being part of this study is furthering the understanding of the impact of the Gulf War participation on the different health symptoms and illnesses that the Gulf War veterans exhibited upon returning from the war.

If you have any questions about the research study, please call me at.For questions about your rights as a study participant, or any concerns or complaints, please contact the University of Phoenix Institutional Review Board

1. As a participant in this study, you should understand the following:

2. You may decide not to be part of this study or you may want to withdraw from the study at any time. If you want to withdraw, you can do so without any problems.

Your identity will be kept confidential.

The researcher has fully explained the nature of the research study and has answered all of your questions and concerns.

If interviews are done, they may be recorded. If they are recorded, you must give permission for the researcher, , to record the interviews. You understand that the information from the recorded interviews may be transcribed. The researcher will develop a way to code the data to assure that your name is protected.

Data will be kept in a secure and locked area. The data will be kept for three years, and then destroyed. The results of this study may be published.

"By signing this form, you agree that you understand the nature of the study, the possible risks to you as a participant, and how your identity will be kept confidential. When you sign this form, this means that you are 18 years old or older and that you give your permission to volunteer as a participant in the study that is described here."

(o) I accept the above terms. (o) I do not accept the above terms. (CHECK ONE)

Signature of the interviewee ____________________ Date _________

Signature of the researcher ____________________ Date _________

APPENDIX C

Confidentiality Statement

To: Veterans Service Organization and VA Hospital

As a researcher working on the above research study at the University of Phoenix, I understand that I must maintain the confidentiality of all information concerning all research participants as required by law. Only the University of Phoenix Institutional Review Board may have access to this information. "Confidential Information" of participants includes but is not limited to: names, characteristics, or other identifying information, questionnaire scores, ratings, incidental comments, other information accrued either directly or indirectly through contact with any participant, and/or any other information that by its nature would be considered confidential. In order to maintain the confidentiality of the information, I hereby agree to refrain from discussing or disclosing any Confidential Information regarding research participants, to any individual who is not part of the above research study or in need of the information for the expressed purposes on the research program. This includes having a conversation regarding the research project or its participants in a place where such a discussion might be overheard; or discussing any Confidential Information in a way that would allow an unauthorized person to associate (either correctly or incorrectly) an identity with such information. I further agree to store research records whether paper, electronic or otherwise in a secure locked location under my direct control or with appropriate safe guards. I hereby further agree that if I have to use the services of a third party to assist in the research study, who will potentially have access to any Confidential Information of participants, that I will enter into an agreement with said third party prior to using any of the services, which shall provide at a minimum the confidential obligations set forth herein. I agree that I will immediately report any known or suspected breach of this confidentiality statement regarding the above research project to the University of Phoenix,

Institutional Review Board.

_(s) __________-__________-__________

Signature of Researcher Printed Name Date

APPENDIX D

Survey Questions

INITIAL INTERVIEW BASELINE SURVEY

1. During military service I was exposed to:
   - ❑ Radioactive Surface Exposure
   - ❑ Sarin or Chemical Agents
   - ❑ Suspected Biological Agents
   - ❑ Other Herbicides
   - ❑ Experimental Vaccines
   - ❑ PB Tablets
   - ❑ Burning Oil Smoke
   - ❑ Insect Borne Diseases
   - ❑ DEET Insecticide
   - ❑ Excess Sand and/or Dust
   - ❑ Contaminated Equipment
   - ❑ Other Detrimental Items

2. Were you exposed to more than one of the above?
   - ❑ Yes
   - ❑ No
   - ❑ Unsure
   - ❑ None

3. Respondent is?
   - ❑ Still able to work
   - ❑ Unable to work
   - ❑ Hospitalized

4. What is your Age?
   - ❑ 30 to 39
   - ❑ 40 to 49
   - ❑ 50 to 59
   - ❑ 60 or over

5. Have you been rated by the VA?
   - ❑ Yes
   - ❑ After years of delay
   - ❑ Rating Denied
   - ❑ Refused to Rate
   - ❑ Pending Completion
   - ❑ Did Not Try

6. What disability area were you rated or you applied for?
   - ❑ Chronic Fatigue Syndrome
   - ❑ Loss of Vision
   - ❑ Post-Traumatic Stress Disorder
   - ❑ Hearing/Ear/Balance Disorder
   - ❑ Bone/Joint Deterioration
   - ❑ Neck/Spine Deterioration
   - ❑ Irritable Bowel Syndrome
   - ❑ Multiple Sclerosis
   - ❑ Unable to Work
   - ❑ Multiple Other Problems

7. Did they rate you for health damage caused during combat service?
   - ❑ Yes
   - ❑ No

8. Have you had Cancers?
   - ❑ o Yes
   - ❑ o No

9. Have you had Cardiac problems?
- ❑ Yes
- ❑ No

10. Have you had Thyroid or Parathyroid problems?
- ❑ Yes
- ❑ No

11. Have you had kidney, liver, or gallbladder problems?
- ❑ Yes
- ❑ No

12. Do you have increasing problems remembering things?
- ❑ Yes
- ❑ No

13. Do you have problems with balance and falling?
- ❑ Yes
- ❑ No

14. Do you have problems with muscle spasms and twitching?
- ❑ Yes
- ❑ No

15. Have you had vision problems?
- ❑ No
- ❑ Lost/Losing Vision
- ❑ Blurred Vision
- ❑ Dimming Vision
- ❑ Distorted/Double Vision

- ❑ 16. Do you have emotional problems as a result of your combat service?
- ❑ No
- ❑ General Panic Attacks
- ❑ Panic with Loud Sounds
- ❑ Severe Depression

17. What other diagnosed problems do you have that you feel were a result of exposure to the agents selected from question 1?

- ❑ None
- ❑ Joint Pain and/or Damage
- ❑ Severe Headaches
- ❑ Severe Stomach Problems
- ❑ Bleeding Blisters
- ❑ Scale/Pustules or Crusts
- ❑ Post-Traumatic Stress Disorder
- ❑ Severe Muscle Pain
- ❑ Nerve Damage
- ❑ Chronic Fatigue Syndrome
- ❑ Various Tumors

18. What treatments have you received?

- ❑ Light Medication
- ❑ Heavy Medication
- ❑ Surgery
- ❑ Surgery and Medication
- ❑ Physical Therapy
- ❑ Emotional Therapy
- ❑ Bad reactions to Medication
- ❑ Nothing Provided

19. What treatments have you tried that have helped with your combat related health damage?

- ❑ Nothing really helps
- ❑ Heavy Medication
- ❑ Special Therapy
- ❑ Surgery
- ❑ Physical Therapy
- ❑ Emotional Therapy
- ❑ Special Air Conditioning
- ❑ Additional Sleep
- ❑ Alternative Medical Treatment
- ❑ Have not tried any

20. Have you had VA doctors or facilities that have truly paid attention to you?

- ❑ Often
- ❑ Occasionally
- ❑ Rarely
- ❑ None

21. What is your Gender?

- ❑ Male
- ❑ Female

22. Did you serve in the Persian Gulf from August 1990 to January 1992?

- ❑ Yes
- ❑ No

APPENDIX E

RAND Health Survey

The RAND 36-Item Health Survey

Table 1

STEP 1: RECORDING ITEMS

ITEM NUMBERS	Change original response category (a)	To recoded value of:
1,2,20,22,34,36	1----------->	100
	2----------->	75
	3----------->	50
	4----------->	25
	5----------->	0
3,4,5,6,7,8,9,10,11,12	1----------->	0
	2----------->	50
	3----------->	100
13,14,15,16,17,18,19	1----------->	0
	2----------->	100
21,23,26,27,30	1----------->	100
	2----------->	80
	3----------->	60
	4----------->	40
	5----------->	20
	6----------->	0
24,25,28,29,31	1----------->	0
	2----------->	20
	3----------->	40
	4----------->	60
	5----------->	80
	6----------->	100
32,33,35	1----------->	0
	2----------->	25
	3----------->	50
	4----------->	75
	5----------->	100

(a) Precoded response choices as printed in the questionnaire.

The RAND 36-Item Health Survey

Table 2

STEP 2: AVERAGING ITEMS TO FORM SCALES

Scale	Number Of Items	After Recoding Per Table 1, Average The Following Items:
Physical functioning	10	3 4 5 6 7 8 9 10 11 12
Role limitations due to physical health	4	13 14 15 16
Role limitations due to emotional problems	3	17 18 19
Energy/fatigue	4	23 27 29 31
Emotional well-being	5	24 25 26 28 30
Social functioning	2	20 32
Pain	2	21 22
General health	5	1 33 34 35 36

The RAND 36-Item Health Survey

Table 3

RELIABILITY, CENTRAL TENDENCY AND VARIABILITY OF SCALES IN THE MEDICAL OUTCOMES STUDY

Scale	Items	Alpha	Mean	SD
Physical functioning	10	0.93	70.61	27.42
Role functioning/physical	4	0.84	52.97	40.78
Role functioning/emotional	3	0.83	65.78	40.71
Energy/fatigue	4	0.86	52.15	22.39
Emotional well-being	5	0.90	70.38	21.97
Social functioning	2	0.85	78.77	25.43
Pain	2	0.78	70.77	25.48
General health	5	0.78	56.99	21.11
Health change	1	---	59.14	23.12

Note: Data is from baseline of the Medical Outcomes Study (N - 2471), except for Health change, which was obtained one year later.

RAND 36-Item Health Survey 1.0 Questionnaire Items

1. In general, would you say your health is:	
Excellent	1
Very good	2
Good	3
Fair	4
Poor	5

2. **Compared to one year ago,** how would your rate your health in general **now**?	
Much better now than one year ago	1
Somewhat better now than one year ago	2
About the same	3
Somewhat worse now than one year ago	4
Much worse now than one year ago	5

The following items are about activities you might do during a typical day. Does **your health now limit you** in these activities? If so, how much?

(Circle One Number on Each Line)

	Yes, Limited a Lot	Yes, Limited a Little	No, Not limited at All
3. **Vigorous activities,** such as running, lifting heavy objects, participating in strenuous sports	[1]	[2]	[3]
4. **Moderate activities,** such as moving a table, pushing a vacuum cleaner, bowling, or playing golf	[1]	[2]	[3]
5. Lifting or carrying groceries	[1]	[2]	[3]
6. Climbing **several** flights of stairs	[1]	[2]	[3]
7. Climbing **one** flight of stairs	[1]	[2]	[3]
8. Bending, kneeling, or stooping	[1]	[2]	[3]
9. Walking **more than a mile**	[1]	[2]	[3]
10. Walking **several blocks**	[1]	[2]	[3]
11. Walking **one block**	[1]	[2]	[3]
12. Bathing or dressing myself	[1]	[2]	[3]

During the **past 4 weeks**, have you had any of the following problems with your work or other regular daily activities **as a result of your physical health**?

(Circle One Number on Each Line)

	Yes	No
13. Cut down the amount of time you spent on work or other activities	1	2
14. **Accomplished less** than you would like	1	2
15. Were limited in the **kind** of work or other activities	1	2
16. Had **difficulty** performing the work or other activities (for example, it took extra effort)	1	2

During the **past 4 weeks**, have you had any of the following problems with your work or other regular daily activities **as a result of any emotional problems** (such as feeling depressed or anxious)?

(Circle One Number on Each Line)

	Yes	No
17. Cut down the **amount of time** you spent on work or other activities	1	2
18. **Accomplished less** than you would like	1	2
19. Didn't do work or other activities as **carefully** as usual	1	2

These questions are about how you feel and how things have been with you **during the past 4 weeks**. For each question, please give the one answer that comes closest to the way you have been feeling.
How much of the time during the past 4 weeks . . .

(Circle One Number on Each Line)

	All of the Time	Most of the Time	A Good Bit of the Time	Some of the Time	A Little of the Time	None of the Time
23. Did you feel full of pep?	1	2	3	4	5	6
24. Have you been a very nervous person?	1	2	3	4	5	6
25. Have you felt so down in the dumps that nothing could cheer you up?	1	2	3	4	5	6
26. Have you felt calm and peaceful?	1	2	3	4	5	6
27. Did you have a lot of energy?	1	2	3	4	5	6
28. Have you felt downhearted and blue?	1	2	3	4	5	6
29. Did you feel worn out?	1	2	3	4	5	6
30. Have you been a happy person?	1	2	3	4	5	6
31. Did you feel tired?	1	2	3	4	5	6

32. During the **past 4 weeks**, how much of the time has your **physical health or emotional problems** interfered with your social activities (like visiting with friends, relatives, etc.)?

(Circle One Number)

All of the time 1

Most of the time 2

Some of the time 3

A little of the time 4

None of the time 5

How **TRUE** or **FALSE** is each of the following statements for you.

(Circle One Number on Each Line)

	Definitely True	Mostly True	Don't Know	Mostly False	Definitely False
33. I seem to get sick a little easier than other people	1	2	3	4	5
34. I am as healthy as anybody I know	1	2	3	4	5
35. I expect my health to get worse	1	2	3	4	5
36. My health is excellent	1	2	3	4	5

APPENDIX F:

Permission to Use an Existing Survey

September 15, 2015
I am a doctoral student from University of Phoenix writing my dissertation tentatively titled GULF WAR SYNDROME'S EFFECTS ON THE WELL-BEING OF PERSIAN GULF VETERANS under the direction of my dissertation committee chaired by. I would like your permission to reproduce to use survey instrument in my research study. I would like to use and print your survey under the following conditions:

I will use this survey only for my research study and will not sell or use it with any compensated or curriculum development activities;

I will include the copyright statement on all copies of the instrument;

I will send my research study and one copy of reports, articles, and the like that make use of these survey data promptly to your attention.

If these are acceptable terms and conditions, please indicate so by signing one copy of this letter and returning it to me either through postal mail, fax, or e-mail:

Sincerely,
Signature

APPENDIX G

Rand Health Inquiries

Thank you for your message. We will do our best to reply to each email we receive, but our response may be delayed. All of the surveys and tools from RAND Health are public documents, available without charge. Please provide an appropriate citation when using these products. No further permissions are necessary.

APPENDIX H

Letter of Introduction

INTRODUCTION: You are invited to participate in a research study entitled "GULF WAR SYNDROME'S EFFECTS ON THE WELL-BEING OF PERSIAN GULF VETERANS. The main investigator of the study is a doctoral student at the University of Phoenix majoring in Management in Organizational Leadership. You were chosen to participate in the study because you may have served in the Gulf War or been in the military between 1990-1992. Approximately 150 participants will be enrolled in this study.

Participation should require about 45 minutes of your time. Participation is entirely voluntary; you may withdraw from the study at any time without any consequences.

PURPOSE: The purpose of this quantitative, correlational study is to examine the different health symptoms and illnesses that the Gulf War veterans exhibited upon returning from the war. Results of the study will be compiled into a research study project that will result in a manuscript for publication. Responses will be completely anonymous, and your identity will not be linked to this survey in any way.

PROCEDURES: If you decide to participate in the study, you will respond to one survey on health issues. If: you do not wish to participate, simply return the surveys to the researcher.

RISKS AND INCONVENIENCES: There are no known major risks to you for participating in this research studies. It may be inconvenient for you to fill out three questionnaires; however, you will receive a ten-dollar gift card for your time.

POSSIBLE BENEFITS: There are no major benefits to you for your participation.

NONDISCLOSURE: Any information that you provide for this research study and any personal information such as your name will not be linked in any way to the surveys. It will not be possible to identify you from any of your responses to the specific information provided for this study.

QUESTIONS: You may ask any questions, at any time, that will help you to better understand how this study will be performed and/or how it will be related to you. You may contact the principal researcher, or by calling. or the investigator's faculty advisor at the University of Phoenix School of Advanced Studies.

Please retain this letter for your records.

APPENDIX I

Non-Disclosure Form

I freely and voluntarily and without any force or coercion, consent to be a participant in the research project entitled "GULF WAR SYNDROME'S EFFECTS ON THE WELL-BEING OF PERSIAN GULF VETERANS. This research is being conducted by who is pursuing a Doctor of Management degree at the University of Phoenix. I understand that the purpose of his research project is to better understand how Service members that served in the Persian Gulf may be suffering with an undiagnosed illness.

I understand that I will participating by taking one survey. My total time commitment for participating in these surveys will be approximately 45 minutes. This information obtained from the surveys will be kept completely confidential. My responses will be analyzed in combination with the answers of other participants in this study at a later date. I understand that the researcher is the only person who will have access to these surveys and that they will be destroyed three years after completion of the research project. I understand that my participation is voluntary, and I may stop participation at any time during the process. All of my answers to the questions will be kept confidential, to the extent allowed by law. If the results of this study are published, my name will not be used in reporting of the results.

I understand that there is no risk involved if I agree to take part in this study. The researcher will be available to talk with me about any concerns while taking part. I am also able to stop my participation at any time during the process. I understand that this consent may be withdrawn at any time without prejudice, penalty, or loss of benefits. I have been given the right to ask and have answered any questions concerning the study. Any questions I may have, have been answered to my satisfaction. If I have questions about this research project, my rights as a participant, or risks involved, I understand that I may contact or the University of Phoenix.

I have read and understand this consent form and agree to take part in this research study.

____________________________ _____________________

(Participant) (Date)

CPSIA information can be obtained
at www.ICGtesting.com
Printed in the USA
JSHW011002201122
33351JS00004B/211

9 798822 904262